Kill Me First

Kill Me First

The Dangerous Side of Alzheimer's

Karen Olivia Peck

Twisted Tree Publishers

This book is intended to provide helpful information on the subjects discussed. It is not meant to be used, nor should it be used, to diagnose or treat any medical condition, and it is not to be construed as legal advice. For information about any medical or legal issue, please consult a professional in the field.

Printed in the United States of America
Design by Meadowlark Publishing Services
ISBN 978-1-4675-0428-7

Published by Twisted Tree Publishers
5060 SW Philomath Blvd., #345
Corvallis, OR 97333

Published 2012

To Doug, Greg, Kris and Steph, and for Maizie,
who was always there

Preface

I've always wanted to write. My brother taught me how to read and write when I was four years old. Since then books have been my obsession. Creating fictional stories was easy for me, but putting them on paper was something else. I did write a book once, but I have to admit it really wasn't any good and it went nowhere. The closest I could come to having a writing career was as a technical writer for a large high-tech company.

Never did I imagine that my own parents would hand me a story of such huge importance that I would have to, need to, write this book: *Kill Me First*.

I barely knew what Alzheimer's disease was, let alone how to deal with someone who had it. There is no Alzheimer's training school to attend and no two Alzheimer's patients are alike, so the advice that is available does not always apply to a standard behavior. All that can be done is to categorize the symptoms to help diagnose Alzheimer's disease through such tests as MRIs and Mini Mental State Exams (MMSEs).

I found that the facts about Alzheimer's are shocking. According to alz.org, Alzheimer's disease is the sixth leading cause of death in the United States. Every sixty-nine seconds someone develops Alzheimer's. Out of the top ten leading causes of death, such as stroke, heart disease, or cancer, Alzheimer's is the only disease that has no cure, no known cause, and no known way to prevent it.

While death rates have fallen for heart attack, stroke, cancer, AIDS, and diabetes, the death rate for Alzheimer's patients has skyrocketed a whopping 66 percent.

As I became more familiar with Alzheimer's and its behaviors, I realized how unprepared we all will be when this epidemic grows to its predicted numbers of one in eight, up from the current one in twenty by 2050.

Close to five and a half million people have Alzheimer's and there are over fifteen million nonpaid caregivers. There is a genetic form of Alzheimer's, referred to as early onset, but more commonly, Alzheimer's has no genetic connection; it just arrives. It is a brain-wasting disease that is a hundred percent fatal.

Logic, reason, and the ability to comprehend consequences are no longer available to the Alzheimer's patient. Depending on which parts of the brain are affected, the patient will remain docile or may become violent. Personalities can change suddenly or not at all. A gentle husband can start beating his wife. Or an ill-tempered, aggressive person can become meek or even fearful. It is most important that we understand that an Alzheimer's patient is no longer capable of being responsible.

As the human brain is laid to waste and neural connections are lost, only grief will arrive for the rest of us.

I was moved to tell this tale because I believe the lessons it contains are important to share with two groups of readers. Those who are currently struggling to help someone close to them who has Alzheimer's disease may find familiar themes. And those who have this situation in their future will encounter warning signs that may help them recognize the disease more quickly than I did. It is my hope that both of these groups will learn the value of creative caregiving and recognize in the financial and legal side of the story a cautionary tale that will help prevent catastrophe. I also hope that this chronicle of the emotional upheaval involved will assure them that they are not alone.

Acknowledgements

My husband, Doug, my brother, Greg, and my daughters, Stephanie and Kristen, are the most important players in this story, but I owe a debt of gratitude to everyone who helped our family.

Good people are not hard to find, as I found so many who, time and time again, never failed us when we needed them. To paraphrase a line from Blanche DuBois in Tennessee Williams's *A Streetcar Named Desire*, I did rely on the kindness of strangers, sometimes hourly.

To those of you who are caregivers and will be caregivers, none of us could survive without your daily offerings of generosity and expertise.

Profound appreciation goes to Meadowlark Publishing Services (Sheridan McCarthy and Stanton Nelson). They have been crucial to the completion of this book.

One

May 11, 2007

It was late evening and the emergency room was crowded. Dad was gasping in pain. He could barely walk, so we found a wheelchair for him.

In the queue ahead of us a father gently rocked his coughing toddler. A mud-splattered man held his bloody arm close to his chest and joked with his friend about their rugby game. A young girl limped behind her mother to the intake desk. CNN was blaring on the wall-mounted television.

Finally it was our turn. Earlier I had received a call from my parents' assisted living facility. Dad had fallen in the shower, and as the day wore on his back pain increased until it hurt to breathe. The doctor ordered X-rays, and Dad was wheeled to the lab. Mom and I sat side by side, crammed in a corner of the tiny exam room on orange plastic chairs never meant for the human form, our shoulders touching. Restless from sitting, I got up and paced the small space for a few minutes, then sat down again next to Mom.

"I got a letter from Uncle George," I said, breaking the silence of the quiet room. "He's doing well and sends his greetings to you." Mom said nothing.

I offered her a dog-eared copy of People dated the previous year. She shook her head and turned away from me, letting me know she wasn't interested in conversation. She stared at her thumbnail and picked at the cuticle.

Slouched in my chair, I counted a total of sixty-three ceiling tiles. I was halfway through counting the floor tiles when Mom spoke.

"I pushed him," she said, staring past me at the wall behind the exam table.

"I pushed him," she repeated. "He made me so mad. I shoved him and he fell."

Five days later, Dad died.

1

Two

I have to type in a four-digit security code to enter the residence area of my mother's Alzheimer's facility. Soon after Dad died, her doctor referred her here. Several times a week I carry in a small tray: one house coffee with half-and-half on the side, and a mocha single shot with extra whipped cream and a straw.

I knock softly before entering her small room. She's in her recliner next to a window, sleeping, her head tilted back on a pale blue neck pillow. Her mouth is open and her hands are resting on her thighs. As the door clicks shut, she wakes up.

"Did you bring me chocolate?"

"I gave five bags of chocolate to one of the aides," I tell her.

She looks disappointed and leans forward in her chair.

"Why not give them to me?" she asks.

"You can't have food in your room when you're alone, Mom," I say. "They won't let me bring it in here, remember? But all you have to do is ask one of the aides and they'll bring you some." I remind her that she has swallowing problems and that state laws prohibit memory care residents from having food when they're alone.

"The coffee here is so lousy," she tells me when I hand over the hot drinks. She sips her mocha first, as it's the coolest. She'll sip at her house coffee when I'm gone, then let it sit until the cream is clotted and it has to be tossed out.

The window next to her chair offers views of the wide Willamette Valley all the way to the Cascade Mountains, but the vertical blinds are almost completely closed. I sit across from her on the corner of her twin bed so she can see me. If I'm out of her visual range, she forgets I'm here.

"So, what's going on?" she asks, slowly coming out of the grogginess of her interrupted nap; it has taken a while for the mocha to perk her up.

3

"Not much. Everyone seems to be fine."

"Say," she says. "I've been wondering what I could have out of my storage, to have here, something of mine that I can enjoy."

I look around her small room. It's crammed with her things: a dresser, desk and chair, twin bed, the chair where she sits, a table, and a tall maple lamp with a large white shade. There is no space to add anything else. And even if there were, the facility limits what residents can have in their rooms: nothing of value, such as jewelry (which can be easily picked up and pocketed by another absent-minded resident); nothing dangerous like scissors; nothing fragile like an antique lamp.

"Sure, Mom," I say. "Tell me what you'd like to have and I'll get it out of storage for you."

She looks around her room, seeking ideas. Her eyes rest on a high bookshelf in the farthest corner of the room. There are three Lladro figurines, beyond her reach, that she and Dad bought in Spain on a trip they took after they retired in the mid-1970s. On the wall above her desk hangs a large oil painting, a pastoral scene of a man fishing from a small boat on a pond. There are a sepia-toned photo taken on Mom and Dad's wedding day and a photograph of Mom's mother and sisters. All of the furniture is hers, including the Stickley pieces she has lovingly cared for since the 1950s. Her six-drawer dresser has a harvest-gold towel draped over the side facing the heating vent on the wall.

"The hot air from that wall vent is burning it," she tells me.

She won't let me remove the towel, although the dresser is three feet away from the vent and quite cool even when she turns the thermostat up to eighty. I don't bother trying to reason with her, tell her that the towel is more flammable than the hardwood beneath it.

"It's not hot, Mom," I say instead.

"It's hot inside," she replies. "My clothes are hot … they're cooking." She looks confused. "Oh, just leave it."

We sit quietly for a while, her wheezy sips on her mocha straw the only sounds in the room.

"It's very dark in here," I say. "Shall I turn on a light or open the blinds?"

"No. I like it dark."

"You're missing a great view of the mountains."

I hear her swallow. She ignores my suggestion to brighten the room.

"Well," I tell her, "I should go."

She doesn't reply. I linger a few more moments, picking up a soiled paper napkin and collecting the plastic water cups she uses to chase down nasty-tasting medications. Because of her difficulty swallowing, her meds have to be liquefied, compounded and mixed with pureed fruit, and administered by a medical aide. The pulverized brew makes her eyes water.

"Say, can I have my purse?" she asks, moving to sit on the edge of her chair.

"Sure, Mom. I'll bring it next time."

Every time I visit she asks for her purse. I tell her "sure," her shoulders relax, and she sits back in her recliner. I'd never imagined that being a caregiver would encourage me to be such a liar, but I find I'm quite good at it.

Mom's purse is one of the many things she can't have anymore. She never remembers she's asked for it, and each time I show up empty-handed. Having a purse had given her hope of leaving this place and returning to a normal life. It could hold all the things that meant she could manage her life: money, a checkbook, a credit card, car keys. At first I'd gone with her caregivers' suggestion that I give her an empty purse so she could put items such as lipstick and tissue in it. But she quickly became obsessed with filling it with things that contained the hope of independent living, and her nagging for them was relentless. It was easier on everyone—not least me—if she didn't have a purse at all.

There is no point in telling her what she can no longer have. To avoid her inevitable disappointment, I just assure her I'll get to it next time I see her.

I move across the room to her closet. Half of it contains her shoes and clothing. The other half contains bedding, towels, personal-hygiene supplies, and latex gloves for the nursing aides to use when they help her shower. I always check the inventory, as Mom never knows what she's out of. Looking over her stock of Polident, Depends, and toothpaste, I say, "I see that you don't need anything for now, Mom."

"Next time you come, you bring me chocolate," she says.

"OK, I will."

Picking up my coat, I take one last look around the room to see if there's anything that needs my attention before I leave. Finding nothing obvious, I am, as usual, happy to be going. Mom's room is so dark and far too warm; I become claustrophobic if I stay there for too long.

"'Bye, Mom. I'll see you in a couple of days."

"OK."

I type in the security code to exit the residence area. Mom no longer follows me to the door like she used to, pushing me from behind and demanding to know when she can get out of there. She no longer pounds on the doors that lock behind me, yelling "Let me go! You let me out of here!" Maybe it's the progression of Alzheimer's, or the medications she takes have helped to calm her down, but Mom has changed since she first came here.

At the reception desk I sign out and wave good-bye to the staff. I draw in a deep breath of fresh air as I walk out the door.

Three

I t's the end of the month. Mom's storage unit is on my way home from her facility, and I stop by the office to pay next month's bill. I decide that as long as I'm there I may as well see if I can find some little memento to cheer her up.

I've reduced the contents to about a fourth of what used to be here; I'm almost done with the organizing, the donating, and the tossing out. Mom was such a hoarder for so long, it's taken me years to make sense of it. I've moved everything in the unit at least four times, at first catering to her whims and then tending to her needs. I know by heart what's in each box and drawer. At least since she entered an Alzheimer's facility I've been able to sort through it all without her standing over my shoulder—which always used to send me to the aspirin bottle and her into a whirlwind of separation anxiety.

What's left are the precious antiques handed down from her side of the family and the things she collected before a brain-wasting disease wrecked her sensibilities.

Prior to moving into memory care, she had blown through a fifty-four-thousand-dollar checking account, buying nothing but trash. She spent her days at bargain stores buying toxically produced instant-landfill items with no value or purpose other than to satisfy her appetite for shopping, her need to simply *have stuff*.

She had filled up the one-bedroom apartment she and Dad shared at the assisted living facility when he was still alive. She stacked up her purchases, leaving boxes and bags unopened, like pyramids, collecting so much that only narrow paths remained in which to navigate through the apartment.

I'm not sure when she crossed the line between collecting and hoarding. Mom once had flawless taste in furniture, antiques, and clothing. But as she grew more ill, she began to mindlessly grab everything in sight and pile it in heaps. And once something was buried, It was forgotten.

At least I can control the hoarding in her room now. She can't shop anymore, so there's no chance of her turning it into another rodent's nest.

Sometimes that feels like the only thing I can control.

Four

There are lovely things in this ten-by-fifteen-foot space. A polished brass chandelier that was given to her parents in 1917 as a wedding gift. A fragile, hundred-year-old china cabinet with curved glass sides. There are books by Emerson, Shakespeare, and Huxley. Her confirmation Bible, written in Finnish, is here. There are antique lamps, china, silverware, a mink coat, and boxes filled with photographs.

Two matching Stickley chairs I've loved since childhood are tucked in a corner. When my dad was elderly and unsteady, he fell on one of them and broke one of its legs away from the frame. I've been thinking that one day I'll have it fixed, maybe replace the fabric.

Atop a stack of cardboard cartons is a spinning wheel from the late 1800s. Mom spent a fortune on it, and to avoid a confrontation with my dad, she hid it at my house for a while. After several months of having to dust it, I had a better idea: I put it in my car and brought it to their home as a birthday gift for her. Dad was not happy about having more of her clutter in their house, but he couldn't refuse the gift.

Tucked inside one of the cartons is a set of berry bowls from her grandmother. On the back they say "Made in Silesia." Once a province of Prussia, Silesia ceased to exist when the map of Europe was redrawn after World War I. These pieces are delicate, their edges slightly wobbly where their maker perhaps stretched or laughed during their creation. The lovely imperfections of hand-thrown pots.

I've flipped through hundreds of photos of Mom and her family; I've seen her hugging her sisters, giggling, playing dress-up. There's a big black-and-white photo of my great grandparents dated 1888. They're sitting on chairs outside their large white farmhouse. Great grandfather is dressed in a three-piece suit. Great grandmother wears a beautiful black dress with beaded detail along the bodice, and her neck is adorned with a long string of pearls.

Their fingers are curled loosely into fists resting on their laps. My guess is that they were trying to hide their hands, which would reveal them as the hard-working farmers they were; grimy fingernails would betray the affluent appearance they were trying for. In the background is the vastness of their dairy farm.

"That's their dog, Dagne," Mom once told me, pointing to a large sheepdog just to the left of the couple. "I hated that dog. It bit me when I was six. Dagne made me afraid of all dogs."

In a desk drawer there are some gold coins and old Bakelite jewelry. The coins cost Mom more than twelve thousand dollars. She bought them just before we moved her into memory care, into an apartment too tiny to accommodate these things, her things.

Lila Olivia Hanka was born on August 14, 1918, three months before the end of World War I. At the time her father was in a field hospital in France healing from shrapnel wounds. He kept a piece of the splintered metal, one that had been removed from his stomach, as a souvenir. I've often held it and I do so again. Even now it can still cut skin. So cold and ugly.

During peacetime Mom's father was an accountant, graduate of a business college. The family lived in a big house, an old Dutch colonial, in Minneapolis. They also had two dairy farms in Minnesota, which provided food for her large extended family during the Great Depression.

"I hated those turnips," Mom often said. "We had turnip everything. It seemed like it was the only thing that grew there."

"Mom," I said once, "I'm sure you had more than turnips. You must have had other food. Did you know that during the Great Depression in the US there was one starvation death every seven minutes? You and your family were fortunate."

She fluttered her hand in my face, waving me away, a familiar dismissive gesture that I hated. It reduced me to trivia, minimized me. And as always, the fact that she could only measure her life by what she didn't have made me angry.

It was impossible to convince her how fortunate she was, though I couldn't seem to stop trying. I made another attempt. "Mom," I said, "none of the women in our family died in childbirth. Only one of their many children died young. All the men who went to war came home. There have been no foreclosures, no bankruptcies, no prison inmates, no epidemics, no murderers or rapists. No one's house burned down, no one was ever unemployed for very long. No one's child was stolen. We're all lucky if you ask me."

"Well, no one is asking you," she sniffed.

Mom and her two younger sisters grew up in a tightly knit Finnish community. She spoke no English until she was six; to attend public school, she had to learn. She spent her summers on the dairy farm in northern Minnesota, where Saturday night saunas were a ritual, the stones heated around a wood fire, water drawn from the well to create steam.

First the women and children bathed and then the men. Afterward in the big kitchen, home-baked delicacies like angel food cake and flakey pastries were served with unending amounts of coffee. Everyone sat around the big table feeling clean and satisfied. Stories were told, farm prices were discussed, and letters from family members still living in the old country were read.

One frequently told story was about my great aunt Saima, one of the last of Mom's Finnish relatives to immigrate to the United States, who lived on the fourth floor of a rooming house in Minneapolis. Auntie Saima was fascinated with processed American food. One of her contributions to the Saturday night gathering was a cake made from a packaged mix.

"It was like a brick," Mom would recall. Auntie Saima had followed the high-altitude directions on the box—because she lived on the fourth floor.

During the Great Depression Mom went to college. In 1939, on a summer break from school, she made a decision that would lead her to my father. She and a friend had heard good things about Sun Valley, Idaho.

They hopped a train and headed west.

Five

There are no possessions from my father's childhood in the storage space, or anywhere. No heirlooms, no toys, no hand-knitted baby bonnets or bronzed walking shoes. I have no photos of Dad as a child with his brothers, playing, being kids. My paternal grandfather was an itinerant worker, ever searching for jobs that would pay enough to feed his family. Grandpa McRoberts was a sheepherder, butcher, carpenter, and part-time handyman. I remember him with a tin box of makings in his shirt pocket. He would take it out once in a while to roll a cigarette, then hold the lighter so close to the brim of his baseball cap it would singe.

Dad, James Marvin McRoberts, was born in the Pacific Northwest, the last of four boys, on May 31, 1914. He arrived three months before the start of World War I.

In the 1980s when my Uncle Cliff, one of Dad's older brothers, was dying of lung cancer, he told me that Dad had honed his foul temper by harassing their overworked mother. "Your father is not one of my favorite relatives," he confessed.

By the time Dad came along, family resources were scarce, not much left over for him. Maybe his aggression made up for what was missing. When he was seventeen he suffered a compound fracture of his left leg. Unable to attend school, he became a tyrant, insisting that his fragile mother comply with his every demand while he was bedridden. After his leg healed, he dropped out of school and traveled from job to job, sometimes shoveling coal on a train or herding sheep in the vast meadows of central Idaho. Eventually he ended up tending bar in Ketchum, Idaho, a small blue-collar town next door to Sun Valley.

After Dad and his three brothers were grown, Grandma and Grandpa McRoberts were finally able to buy a small house in

Idaho. At that time the Union Pacific Railroad was developing Sun Valley. Grandpa, Dad, and Dad's brothers built four small cabins in Ketchum, hoping to rent them out to Sun Valley workers. Their plan was that the cabins would generate income for the family in future years.

Dad worked the day shift in several Ketchum taverns, serving mugs of beer to the locals. At night he bartended at the Sun Valley Lodge, rattling a cocktail shaker and pouring mixed drinks into ice-frosted glasses.

Dad was quite dashing on the ski slopes, athletic enough, in fact, to ski with Olympic star Stein Eriksen. In a photograph of him on skis with Mount Baldy in the background, he looks like he's being filmed for a Hollywood movie. Mom once told me that Averell Harriman of Union Pacific Railroad wanted Dad to help advertise Sun Valley's many activities. He could have been beef-cake on a Sun Valley calendar.

When he had time off, he pursued fly fishing on the Big Wood River. Between the drinking and the fishing, Dad met up with Ernest Hemingway and Gary Cooper.

And then he met my mother.

Six

Mom and Dad met in Sun Valley just before World War II: Dad in his bartender's black slacks and white waistcoat and Mom in her crisp, starched waitress uniform. Off hours, Mom and Dad and their friends rubbed shoulders with the rich and famous on the dance floor of the Challenger Inn as the Hap Miller Orchestra serenaded the Idaho sky with big band music.

"He called me Hank," Mom once told me. "He could never get the Finnish pronunciation of my name. It's h-A-N-k-a-h, not the flat-sounding Hanka that he used to say. The kids in school used to call me Hankie, or worse, Handkerchief. Yes, your father called me Hankie too, but mostly I was Hank to him." She laughed and said, "But that was so long ago and things change, I suppose. He hasn't called me anything nice in quite a while."

Mom may have been an excellent student and brilliant stenographer when she lived in Minnesota, but her skills as a waitress were lacking. She was fired from her job at the Sun Valley Lodge when she told the cofounder of Sun Valley, Count Felix Schaffgosch, that she had no idea what pheasant under glass or pressed duck were. She snickered when he asked if those items were on the menu—she had taken him literally.

"All I could think of was an ironing board and a duck," she would say. "Who would want to press a duck?"

She took a train back to Minneapolis, but Sun Valley had an employee shortage at the time, so after a couple of months the lodge hired Mom back. She was fired several more times, each time going home to Minneapolis then bouncing back to Idaho. The old letters I've found among my mother's things indicate that she made these back-and-forth trips for about two years.

The last time she left Sun Valley, Dad wrote her a letter. The stamp has long since fallen off the envelope, and the only date visible is 1940. It's written on stationery from the Challenger Inn, Sun Valley, Idaho.

> Dearest Hank,
> Well I supposed by now you are a big city girl again.
> Well I hope you like it honey and I hope you don't miss this joint too much, but I hope you miss me like hell.
> Say, that conductor was pretty "hot" at us last nite. He didn't give you any trouble, did he?
> It is now 7 o'clock a.m. and I am slaving away. Every once in a while I write a couple of sentences and then honey I go out to look for Hank in the hall, but she isn't there, she's back in Minn. with the rest of the damn Finns.
> God, I miss you. I very near got on the train with you, but I guess it wouldn't have done me any good, would it.
> Well, goodbye Hank, write to me and think of the wild Irishman once in a while.
>
> All my love,
> Jimmie

While Mom was back in Minneapolis, this time working as an executive secretary, Dad moved to Los Angeles. In the Ketchum tavern where Dad poured beer, Ernest Hemingway had been reading the *L.A. Times* and mentioned to Dad that there were a lot of jobs listed in the classified section. By then Dad was tired of serving drinks, so he and a friend drove to California. Lockheed Aircraft was ramping up for the war in Europe. Dad was hired as an apprentice machinist.

Several nights after the attack on Pearl Harbor, the Glenn Miller Orchestra was playing "It Happened in Sun Valley" on national radio. Coincidentally, Mom and Dad were listening to the same radio station at the same time. Her phone rang in Minneapolis. He proposed and she took the next available train to California.

Mom and Dad were married at the L.A. County Courthouse on

January 5, 1942, less than a month after Pearl Harbor. They lived in a bungalow apartment only a few blocks away from downtown Hollywood. Mom found the same glamour and excitement in L.A. she had found in the resort town of Sun Valley. Photographs I've looked at often show them in stylish clothes posing in front of the opulent Grauman's Chinese Theater, picnicking at Griffith Park, and standing on the corner of Hollywood and Vine. Mom dressed in gorgeous suits, Dad in sport coats and slacks with black-and-white wingtip shoes, his dark curly hair slicked back.

"I loved L.A." Mom often said. "It was like Minneapolis with the museums, the libraries, and the theaters. It was also like the Sun Valley night life."

My brother Greg was born at Queen of Angels Hospital in L.A. just before the end of World War II in 1945. After the war, Lockheed started handing out pink slips, and my dad lost his job. Thousands of GIs were returning and competing for jobs. Government contracts were drying up, and the postwar economy was in a slump. All of the luxury items once purchased with Mom's paychecks became impossible to obtain after she quit her job as an executive secretary at Atlantic Richfield. Then, four months after my brother was born, Mom was pregnant with me.

"We tried all the birth control available, condoms. I had a diaphragm but you came along anyway," she often told me when I was old enough to understand, usually while brushing my unbrushable hair.

"Your hair is just like your grandmother's," Mom would say, referring to Gramma Minnie, my dad's mother. She had curly hair and lots of it, which turned pure white when she was older. She tried to control it by piling it up on her head, and even then it defied the constraints of bobby pins and hairpins. My hair rebelled against rubber bands and the cheap home permanents Mom used to try to straighten my hair. "Nothing works," she would frown. "Your hair cannot be tamed."

Each brush stroke that landed on my head came a bit harder than the one before as she got deeper into her story of my beginnings. I carried a sense of guilt for decades, feeling that my appearance in the world had somehow upset my mother's careful plans, and these insecurities plagued me well into my adult years. My mother-in-law was sympathetic when I told her this story. "Just be glad that you're here," she told me. "Without you we would not have your daughters, so don't go worrying about what your mother said. She's just angry at your dad, that's all."

"Yes," I had to agree. "She's always been mad."

My arrival was a great inconvenience for Mom. And soon afterward, Dad would go missing in action on the home front.

When I was three months old and Greg was sixteen months, Mom and Dad left Los Angeles. We moved to Ketchum, where Dad went back to bartending and Mom looked after us. Dad resumed skiing and fishing and was rarely available for domestic life.

Now Mom was isolated with two babies in one of Grandpa's small cabins. She had winter snowstorms to contend with instead of California sun. She had to learn how to drive a car in an Idaho blizzard.

Gone were the beautiful suits she used to wear to work. Gone was her paycheck that bought the extras. And Dad was meeting a lot of women, many of whom were bored, dragged to Idaho by their husbands only to be abandoned while the men went on long fishing trips.

Ketchum was still ruggedly masculine, and cheating was an accepted fact of life. The only person Dad's transgressions bothered was Mom. Not even Dad's mother thought it was a problem. Mom kept all of her letters, and it was in one of them that I found my grandmother's advice to her: stay with your philandering husband.

Around the time of my first birthday Mom walked into a tavern where Dad was bartending and caught him in a passionate embrace with "some babe," as she would later refer to his girlfriends. She packed a suitcase and, with my brother and me in tow, rode a train to Minnesota.

Her plan was to live in her parents' house in Minneapolis. Our grandmother would babysit us while Mom worked and she would pay rent and help with the household chores. But our grandfather had a major stroke, which changed everything for Mom. Grandma was worried about the prospect of two tiny children running around my largely paralyzed grandfather

"It's best that you and your children return to your husband," she told Mom.

Having nowhere else to go, Mom returned to Ketchum. It was the late 1940s and the Cold War was just beginning. A hotter war was taking place in our house.

Years later, my brother and I watched *Victory at Sea* on TV and hardly blinked. The great battles were in our hallway, or kitchen, or living room. Our parents' angry words penetrated the walls, echoing off the foundation and framing into my room late at night, filling the spaces with bitterness and hatred. Even the noise of a busy street through an open window couldn't buffer their malicious sniping.

Like most wars, theirs started out small. Their skirmishes were subtle at first, with just my brother and me as their audience. They shushed each other: "Careful, the kids will hear you." But then they got comfortable with the name-calling, the insults, and the mistrust. Broad frontal assaults for the smallest infraction eventually led to trench warfare; in our house, duck and cover were practiced maneuvers. Sides were chosen. When my brother and I tried to remain neutral, we became misaligned allies of the enemy. When we were older, my brother and I disappeared into the neighborhood, refugees seeking asylum in other people's homes.

Each year my parents became more embittered, more willing to publicly punish each other with angry words, ridicule, and embarrassment, their one-upmanship becoming a craft. Throughout my adult years, before saying hello or how are you, Mom's first words to me were, "You cannot believe what *It* did last night." Or last year, or last weekend, or last hour. By then Dad was either "It," "Him," the "Ol' Boy," or "the Bastard."

Dad frequently called Mom the C-word; my brother Greg and I learned all the curse words at home. TV and movies were censored, but our home was rich in foul language. Dad could swear better than anyone. Mom didn't cuss, but her words were stilettos, stabbing and wounding like Grandpa's shrapnel, leaving Dad with no recourse but to flee into a bottle of scotch or cheap wine, or out the door.

Their cruelty bruised our world. Our young lives were trapped within the wounded walls of their house. Their curses fouled the air we breathed. We knew we could leave eventually, and we did. They stayed together and ruined what was left of their lives. Every day their practiced and perfected methods of torture were like fallout after a detonation, shards hanging in the air ready to fall and pierce.

"Just a high school dropout," she would whisper to a friend. "If *It* had a better paying job we'd have the house that I wanted."

Dad, of course, would hear this and strike back with, "Lila, you stupid cunt."

"If *It* had any decency *It* would just die," Mom would whisper. "And he's a drunk too."

Who knows what happens to the marriage bed when the wife has been pregnant for the better part of two years. Mom often mentioned that she felt haggard and unattractive after Greg and I were born. Her beautiful clothes were replaced with dungarees covered with baby food and Idaho mud. The excitement of the cocktail hour and late night dancing was replaced by teething infants, childhood fevers, and sleepless nights.

There is a small snapshot of Mom sitting on the concrete stoop in front of the Ketchum cabin. She's dressed in shorts and an ill-fitting shirt. Greg and I have dirty faces. Mom's hair is frizzed and she wears no makeup, no lipstick. Her lovely face looks tired and defeated. The note on the back of the photo says, "Greg 16 months, Karen 3 months, Me. We look like savages."

Years later, when I was grown up and she was worn down, I asked her why she married Dad.

"He looked like a movie star. My family, everyone said so. He was almost as handsome as my own father."

Maybe it's accidental that my parents' birthdays frame the start and stop of World War I like parentheses. That World War II sparked their I-do's further underscores the foreshadowing of their many battles. Their marriage moved along the same time line as the Cold War, escalation and retreat.

For most participants who are fighting a war, the initial reason for discord obscures with time. When the combatants are deeply immersed in battle, the cause, effect, and exit strategy don't register, only the plan for revenge, the next assault. With nurturing and daily investment, conflicts become distorted and grow to huge proportions. It is the continuation of unforgivable acts that keeps the combat going.

Seven

Greg was seven and I was six when we left Idaho and moved back to L.A. Dad was now a journeyman machinist at Lockheed, which had hired a workforce for the escalating Korean War. Greg and I missed Idaho. Grandpa McRoberts' cabins were close to the wilderness, and every day we climbed hills, followed streams, and watched the seasons change. During the winter we made angels in the snow. In the summer we hiked the Elkhorn Valley and looked for agates.

Greg had turned six in Idaho and entered the first grade, and I was stuck at home. Idaho didn't provide kindergarten, so Greg homeschooled me, sharing his advanced knowledge and taking the mystery out of deciphering letters and words. The Dick and Jane books enthralled me. The Bobbsey Twins were to die for.

The L.A. school district wanted me to stay behind a year because I hadn't been to kindergarten, but Mom was insistent. "She can read and write and knows her numbers," she told the school registrar. They let me into first grade, and Greg advanced to second.

Everything in Southern California was different from the world I had known. In autumn I waited for snow to fall and icicles to form. Instead the Santa Ana winds came, warm and dry. Winter without cold was very strange. There were cars everywhere, and other people's houses were right next door to ours. The neighbors were so close I could hear their infants crying and smell their food.

Everyone's yard was fenced and I was not allowed to walk on anyone's lawn. There were no views of mountains, no meadows to hike through, and there was no secret pond to visit.

Many of Mom and Dad's Idaho crowd also moved to Southern California, taking advantage of the job market. Mom and Dad entertained a lot in their small tract house, hosting cocktail parties, barbecues, and potlucks. On weekends the drink cart was wheeled out early in the day. Dad's first drink made him happy. By the fourth or fifth he was angry and nasty. He didn't care what he said or did. The next day he would be so hung over he'd shake.

Reigning over the backyard, standing at the grill with the other men, Dad would point out Mom's flaws.

"Ya know," he would slur to a friend, "my wife has the ugliest belly I've ever seen." Maybe it was Dad's lack of interest in us that kept him from realizing that his tiny wife had had two large babies—his babies—back to back.

Mom's third or fourth drink reduced her to a one-woman pity party. She would start her anti-Dad whispering campaign in the kitchen.

"He never finished high school. If he had his diploma or if he went to college, we could have a bigger house instead of this cracker box, ya know wha' I mean?" she'd say, her tongue thick with drink. "He couldn't even finish night school."

She ignored the fact that Dad was pinned down at Lockheed for the duration of the war. American manufacturers needed a workforce, and Lockheed's occupational deferment barred him from putting on a uniform. He could neither enlist nor be drafted, although he tried to enlist and received draft notices several times; he did not remain a civilian by choice. After the war there were no GI Bill benefits such as low-cost mortgages and college tuition. Dad got through life entirely on his own.

Greg and I had started getting sick while we still lived back in Idaho. For Greg it was sinus and ear infections. There was a time when he couldn't hear at all. I could put my mouth next to his ear and practically yell and he couldn't hear a word. I had to touch him to get his attention and stand in front of him so he could read my lips.

Greg had surgery at the Sun Valley Hospital to remove his adenoids, and that seemed to improve his hearing for a while, but his problems recurred. For my part, I had sinus problems too, and constant chest infections.

Mom and Dad and their friends were all heavy smokers and because Idaho winters were harsh and long, we kept the windows closed for most of the year. Cigarette smoke hung in the rooms of our tiny house. Our car windows were always rolled up too, and the car would fill with a smoky haze.

In our California house we opened up the windows, even the front door had a screen. We could roll the car windows down and feel the San Fernando Valley breezes on our faces. But we still kept getting sick. Greg had more hearing problems and underwent another surgery to remove his tonsils.

I was so sick with bronchial pneumonia that I missed most of my first and second grade years. Mom and Dad went to work and Greg went to school, so I was alone all day, except when a tutor came to our house to keep me up to speed with school and give me homework. That helped occupy my time. Otherwise, *I Love Lucy* and *I Married Joan* were my companions. *Queen for a Day* was another one of my favorites, depressed ladies winning prizes for their sad tales. I reenacted their stories to an invisible audience with my Betsy McCall paper dolls.

When Greg came home I perked up, eager to hear what he had learned that day. Sometimes he rushed off for his paper route, but he always gave me something to study first. When Mom and Dad came home I abandoned the TV and scurried back to bed, pretending to be napping.

During the worst of my illness I had harsh, wracking coughs that gave me headaches and made me gag. When I spiked a fever Mom called the doctor, who injected penicillin into my skinny butt. It took days for the pneumonia to subside. The coughing hurt my chest, and the sight of greenish phlegm, sometimes streaked with blood, made me cry.

The coughing kept Dad awake, and that would not do. "Lila! Can't you keep that kid quiet!?" he would yell.

I had my first drink before my fifth birthday. To stop my coughing Mom poured Jim Beam whiskey into a teacup, mixed it with hot water and held the cup while I sipped the potent drink. It quieted me down, and I'd fall into a deep sleep. I often wet the bed, though, simply too drowsy to get to the bathroom. "Karen," Mom would say when she saw what I had done, "shame on you!"

After being home for long periods of time, it was always difficult to fit back into the social hierarchy of grade school. But by the time I was in the third grade, at least my health had improved. My report card from that year shows that I finally attended for a full school year.

One Christmas Greg and I got new Schwinn three-speed bikes, real racing bikes with gears and handbrakes. Those bikes were freedom for us. Our parents would not, or could not, take us anywhere if our activities conflicted with their work schedules. While they encouraged our after-school activities, they didn't get involved in them. They were always tired from work, and their cocktail hour was the first thing they pursued after arriving home.

Having bikes allowed us to join scouting groups and spend time at our friends' homes. In the summer we stayed outside until ten or eleven, collecting June bugs that crashed into our hair, playing hide-and-go-seek, or sitting on the grass telling ghost stories, holding a flashlight under our chins. Once a week in the summer months a pale blue station wagon picked us up and took us to day camp, or to ranches where TV cowboys filmed their shows. During the rest of the year we thrived in scouting, which offered us camping and weekly meetings. I learned to swim and became strong. Water ballet was my favorite activity of all.

On our bikes we chased down the bread truck and bought a dozen donut holes for a quarter. We waved furiously at the ice cream truck to ensure that he would stop for us. We rode our Schwinns to the nearby Piggly Wiggly market and bought peanut butter and white bread for lunch. Next to the market there was a barber shop, and I stood in line with the boys to have my hair cut short, finally taming it with a hair gel called Dippity Doo.

At the liquor store we bought candy and cold Nesbitt's orange sodas. Greg and his friends voted for their favorite Miss Rheingold girl. On Saturdays we went to the Reseda Theater and watched double features with cartoons. Sometimes they held raffles; winning tickets would get us a free candy bar or soft drink. Greg and I had so much fun when it was just him and his friends. When it came to being with my own gender, though, things were awkward.

During the school year I found the girlhood hierarchy a mystery. Girls gossiped about their best friends. Being with other girls was frustrating, especially when they played house, which they seemed to do endlessly. I couldn't understand the pretend thing that they seemed to love. Other girls told me what to do, how the dolly mommies and dolly daddies were supposed to act, but I had my own ideas, and they criticized the scenarios I chose to act out with dolls.

Mom had felt completely comfortable telling Greg and me about the facts of life: nothing too graphic, but enough so we knew where babies came from. So it seemed natural to include the birds and bees in my stories. But when I said the word "intercourse," the girls went crying to their mommies, and those mommies asked me to leave making me more confused than ever. It seemed natural to me that mommy and daddy dollies would have babies.

When my dolly dads and moms fought, the girls who were supposed to be my friends banished me. The fighting must have upset them, but nothing about their way of playing house was familiar to me. Their mommy and daddy dollies smooched, held hands, and called each other "Honey."

It was so much easier to be outside with the boys; their games were simpler. If you were a good guy, you killed the bad guys. If you were a bad guy, you died.

At home Greg and I were latchkey kids, used to having the house mostly to ourselves. And that was fine with us. When we were around our parents their criticism was constant. I grew weary of Mom plucking at my hair and telling me to stand up straight. One day I overheard her asking one of her friends, "Do you think Karen is pretty?" I wondered why she couldn't provide that answer for herself. And I was tired of Dad's disapproval. "You stupid knucklehead. Can't you do anything right?" was typical, and it applied to just about everything I did, from table manners to mowing the lawn to riding a bike. My face would burn with humiliation.

When I was in the fourth grade I punched a girl named Cindy, the playground bully. She had tormented me once too often, calling me "skinny." I got in one good blow, my puny fist crashing into her large face, but when I hauled back to do it again, I tripped over her foot and fell on my arm, fracturing my wrist. My attack was premeditated. I had hoped that the act of striking back, of finally reducing a bully to tears, would be gratifying. Cindy shrieked and wailed after my assault, and I took some satisfaction in that, but my arm was sore for a long time after.

Mom was at work when the school called to tell her I'd fallen, and she told them to let my brother walk me home and she would meet me there. I howled for the entire six blocks we had to walk, cradling my arm in a flimsy sling put together by the school nurse. Mom arrived as promised and took me to the doctor, who put my arm in a cast. Eight weeks later I was good as new.

Around that time I began to blossom as a person, to come into my own, and I did well in school. I'm sure Greg had a lot to do with my success. He was fascinated by so much in the world, and he passed his exciting discoveries on to me. He continued to offer me lessons on what he was learning, and that gave me an advantage over the other kids.

By the time I was in the sixth grade I was an athletic A student and getting along with the school crowd. But I also had nightmares, terrifying dreams about my parents dying, usually by committing acts of violence upon one another: Dad beating Mom, or Mom causing an accident that killed Dad. I was only about twelve or thirteen when I had my first clear realization that my parents were truly capable of this.

In the late 1950s Dad was transferred to the San Francisco Bay Area, taking a job with Lockheed Missiles and Space in Sunnyvale. Mom worked for the Cupertino Union School District. They bought a bigger tract home in San Jose: three bedrooms, two bathrooms, two-car garage, front yard, and a backyard with a fence. We were surrounded by neighbors.

L.A. was a desert compared to the lushness of Idaho, but San Jose was a moonscape compared to L.A.

Our L.A. neighborhood had had mature landscaping, and there was an old elm tree in the backyard. The houses were all designed differently. The houses in our new neighborhood were all alike, painted in a pathetic array of pastels. Old orchards had been scooped away, leaving barren substrates on which to build cookie-cutter homes. They seemed to stick up out of the bleak earth like headstones in a deserted cemetery.

I didn't make new friends when we moved to San Jose. I became terribly shy. I had no Girl Scout clubhouse to go to. There were no swimming pools where I could practice water ballet. I couldn't ride my bike around. I didn't know the area, and I feared getting lost. I spent most of my time in my bedroom.

My grades began to slip. In seventh grade I ranked honorable mention instead of honor roll. By eighth grade I was getting B's and C's. I learned how to forge Mom's signature on my report cards. To avoid ridicule and criticism when my parents were home, I attempted to be an invisible child. "Man, your ass sure is getting big," Dad would say as I struggled through puberty. I wore at least three sweaters to hide my bra straps, and had horrible posture, shrinking into myself. I couldn't stop cutting my hair, and then I'd let it grow long again to hide my acned face, which I picked at constantly. By the time I was a junior in high school I was flunking out, cutting school, and preoccupied with how miserable I was, forgetting that I had once been a successful athlete and straight-A student.

I rarely ventured outside my room when Mom and Dad were home. Once in a while I'd use the phone in their bedroom, standing up as I talked so as not to leave any other trace of my being there. My butt print on their bedspread would have invited scorn.

I didn't like being in that room anyway; it always smelled boozy from late-night drinking, and the odor mingled with tobacco smoke, permeating the walls and fabrics. I had few friends to call, and I rarely opened up about myself to them. Mostly, I listened.

At last I discovered the lower rung of the campus student body, smart-ass kids who weren't afraid to say what they thought and I hung out with them. They smoked and swore and acted like thugs and spent a lot of time in detention. I could fire off some zingers that impressed this crowd. I felt popular again.

One day after school when I was sixteen, Dad and I were both home. He came into my room and demanded that I wash his car. "You got it dirty—*you* get to wash it!" I zinged. He became enraged, and I snapped too. We both lost it. There we stood, about a foot apart, screaming, cussing, and neither of us hearing. To shut me up he grabbed my throat with both hands. I kept swearing at him, calling him everything I could think of even after my voice had died to a whisper. When Mom came home, I was still calling him names, soundlessly, merely mouthing the words: "You are the world's biggest prick, you fucking bastard!"

"Jim! *What are you doing?*"

With that, Dad let me go. I stumbled to the garage and rode my bike to a friend's house two miles away. I lied to her parents, saying Mom and Dad were out of town and I was lonely in the empty house, but the bruises on my arms and neck told their own story and they let me stay. I was MIA for almost a week.

Then Mom called me to say that Dad had moved out, and I figured it was safe to come home. A week later, though, plans changed. "Your father and I went to counseling," Mom said. "He told the counselor he didn't need anyone's help. And he's moving back here. We can work together and solve our own problems without strangers poking their noses in our business."

There was no further discussion. There was no police intervention or any other official acknowledgment of what my father had done to me. Dad just moved back. I confined myself to quarters, invisible once again.

But one thing, at least, worked in my favor: I got my driver's license. Now I could go wherever I wanted. I easily learned to disconnect the odometer, and Mom and Dad never knew how many miles I put on their cars.

I fled to Santa Cruz as much as possible, skipping school and getting bad grades. Not only was I immersed in my own failure, but high school helped me forget that education was even important. We students were required to walk in tedious lockstep, following foolish and pointless rules. Girls were made to wear dresses, and hemlines had to be a certain length. Whenever a teacher told us high school would be the best years of our lives, I couldn't believe how depressing that news was.

One day as I was walking down the hallway, the dean of girls demanded that I kneel on the ground. This provided a yardstick for measuring hemlines: if your hem didn't touch the ground

while you were kneeling, humiliated, in full view of other students, you were sent home. I was still growing, and the dress I
had bought the previous summer with my babysitting money was
now a bit too short. This was a breaking point for me. From then
on, every opportunity I had, I ditched school.

Surprisingly, they let me graduate with a 1.2 GPA. At least
that ordeal was over. But I had nowhere to go after high school
and I continued to live in a war zone at home.

Eight

Two years after my high school graduation my best friend was killed by a drunk driver. We had become friends at a party the summer after we graduated. We barely knew each other during our four years of high school, but we bonded when I held her hair off her face as she puked into a toilet at a frat party in downtown San Jose.

She and I had been planning to find an apartment together. After her death I flunked out of a local junior college that had admitted me on academic probation. It was the mid-1960s, and San Francisco was so exciting then. A nineteen-year-old knows nothing about grieving, so I partied, and partied, and partied some more. I drank, smoked cigarettes, tried pot, liked it, and drank and smoked some more. I got stoned and sat slack-jawed as Janis Joplin and Jefferson Airplane rocked my sorrowful life away.

My girlfriends and I hung out with former classmates who formed rock groups called things like the Chocolate Watchband and the Syndicate of Sound. I drove Dad's 1959 baby-blue Hillman Minx convertible and was ever so cool. I'd get drunk, and with a cigarette fixed between my lips, race over Highway 17 to Santa Cruz in borrowed fast cars, never touching the brake pedal, just downshifting to slow around the curves. I was fearless.

The summer after my friend died, a guy I went to high school with returned from a four-year stint in the Navy during the Vietnam War, which he spent patrolling the South China Sea. We got drunk on Cuervo Gold. And got pregnant. I was twenty.

To my surprise, Mom and Dad were supportive, actually excited about having a grandchild. "It's not like you're only fourteen years old and three months gone," Mom said when I gave her the news. I married, and seven months later my daughter was born. Hubby and I bought a small house using his GI benefits.

Three years later my second daughter was born. By her first birthday, my marriage was a mess. Hubby was drinking heavily and gambling. I was sneaking drinks, looking for that comfy, snuggly place I used to go to when Mom dosed me with Jim Beam. I was twenty-five with two children, no education, no job, no car, and a mortgage I could not afford.

I borrowed money from Mom and Dad so I could buy my ex out of his half of our house. At least my daughters and I would have a place to live as long as I could keep up the payments.

I applied for jobs with big employers like Hewlett Packard and Lockheed. I was offered positions but they were all night shifts. I had no one to take care of my daughters. There were no day care services then for infants who were still in diapers or children whose mothers worked at night. Even if there had been, I couldn't afford the cost of care for two kids.

Instead I found a part-time job with the school district and applied for welfare and food stamps to supplement my tiny income. Some months it was almost impossible to make my hundred-and-fifty-dollar house payment.

I continued to get bronchitis. After my divorce and during a flu epidemic, I was desperately sick: within a three-month period I had two cases each of bronchitis and strep throat. And I began to worry about who would watch out for my kids if anything happened to me. I asked my parents to sign on to the deed to my house so that if I died, my daughters' meager inheritance would be protected instead of gambled away by their father, who had not yet settled down. Despite all else, my parents were financially responsible people who worked every day, paid their bills, and saved what they could. They agreed to sign.

When my health returned I dated from time to time, but most guys weren't interested in a twenty-something on welfare with two kids. They appreciated that I kept my house clean, but they could see that I was broke. Most of my dates were guys who had recently graduated from college and were looking for Miss Right, not a former Mrs.

I met one guy who was comfortable with my kids, and we both liked to camp and fish. On the weekends we went to the

Sierras, fried up trout, and drank beer while my daughters caught frogs and waded over slippery rocks in the clear mountain river water.

Mom and I had some horrible fights over this new relationship. Within weeks of my divorce from my first husband, she got into the habit of coming over to my house every day on her way home from work. Upon arriving at my front door, she always began her conversations with "You will never guess what that bastard did last night." She'd stay until late at night, smoking my cigarettes and drinking the wine I could barely afford for myself. When I hid my tiny stash and told her I was fresh out, she started bringing her own supply.

Every day for three years, Mom was at my house. Even my kids grew weary of their grandmother. "She's *always* here," they'd tell me. She wouldn't leave until it was close to Dad's bedtime.

I was in my late twenties during this time and very tired of her. I felt guilty because she always helped me when I asked—and I always needed help. But her demands were huge. For example, I was expected to clean her house, top to bottom, every week. I felt like a child having to clean my parents' bathrooms, do their dishes, and scrub their kitchen floor.

On my thirtieth birthday my new partner and I went to my parents' house and told them we were going to live together for a while.

"I will put the kibosh on that right now," Mom said.

"Mom, I am thirty years old. You cannot run my life. You will not put the kibosh on anything."

That was when Mom disowned me.

"Shame on you, living together. You have no family. Get out."

"Yeah, get out," Dad chimed in.

Months later on Christmas day, my partner and I went to my parents' house and told them we were thinking about a spring wedding and we'd be pleased if they would attend. Mom went into planning mode and told me they would pay for a country club wedding for us. From that point forward, our wedding was out of our hands.

I had been unable to pay back much of the money I'd borrowed from them and I was reluctant to burn bridges again. I acquiesced. But I was also afraid that Mom would add my wedding costs to the tab I had run up.

When I'd borrowed money from them at the time of my divorce, California real estate was crawling at a snail's pace. Later, when I sold my house, the Bay Area technology industry was just starting to move along and home values were rising, slightly but steadily. Instead of the five thousand dollars' equity I had when I divorced, I now had thirty thousand dollars' worth. My daughters were growing, and we needed a bigger house. My soon-to-be husband and I needed every dime to be able to afford a new place. The old place sold within a week. Some guy from IBM was buying up my cheap neighborhood.

"Your house is the thirty-ninth house he's bought here," my realtor told me. I passed that news on to my parents when I told them my house had sold.

"Yeah," Dad said. "I always knew that neighborhood would be valuable one day. Those houses will be torn down to make way for new ones, a shopping mall, and businesses. Whoever owns one of those, owns gold."

We had found a new house, and the escrow process automatically transferred the down payment amount from my old house to the new one. The remainder of my equity would be in a check at the escrow office made payable to Dad, Mom, and me. I couldn't cash that check without their signatures; their names were on the deed just as I had asked.

The morning the escrow check became available, Dad called me. He had gone to the escrow office before it opened and waited, and since he was one of the payees they had to release it to him. I had planned to pay back Mom and Dad out of my portion of the money and start a small college fund for my daughters.

If there was anything left over I would put a down payment on a new car. My old one was constantly breaking down. One night I was driving home from a friend's house and the engine died. My alternator and battery were in such bad shape that the car was shutting down as I drove it. I could keep it going if I turned off the headlights, only turning them back on when I went through intersections. By the time I got home, my daughters were crying, fearful that someone would hit us as we drove home in the dark.

It was a little after eight in the morning when Dad called.

"I have a check here for almost eight thousand dollars," Dad said. I remained quiet, scared of what was to come and knowing his foul temper could explode like a fifty-caliber anti-aircraft gun. I squeezed the phone in my hand and waited for the ack-ack-ack of his attack.

"Where's the rest of it?" Dad demanded. "Where's the rest of my money?"

I told him what Mom had said earlier: "It's not right to make money off of family, so we won't charge you interest. You pay back exactly what you borrow."

"Dad," I said, "I only owe you thirty-five hundred dollars. The rest is mine and the girls'."

"Bullshit," he said. "We became owners of your house when we bailed your ass out."

"But Dad, I've made *all* the house payments for the last seven years. You and Mom have made none. You've never paid property taxes or insurance or mowed the lawn, or ..."

"We bought out your ex's half of the house, so you owe us half of the equity. I calculate that you owe me another ten thousand dollars."

"Dad ..."

"Shut up!" he yelled. "You owe me the rest of that money, you little bitch, you stupid cunt."

He continued to yell, using the same foul words he used on Mom. I screamed back that he was a bastard. He shouted that I was a disgusting failure, a loser.

Mom called later, taking his side, and scolded me for using such foul language. Since there was no contract, I could only remind her of what she'd said: "You told me that family doesn't make money off of each other. You said that I only had to pay back what I borrowed."

"Oh, no I didn't. I never said that. I would never tell you that."

I was paying the price for evicting her from my old home, her refuge from Dad. I tearfully told my new husband that all that money we had counted on, over five thousand dollars, was no longer available—that I had to sign it over to my parents. I

couldn't cash or deposit that check without all three of our signatures on it. If I kept it, it would remain a useless piece of paper
with names and numbers on it.

"At least if you sign it," he responded, "you'll no longer owe
anything to your folks. You'll be free, and your mother can't hold
anything over you."

On a Saturday morning I went over to my parents' house to
sign the check. I knew Dad wouldn't be home, that he was up early for his Saturday morning foursome at their club. Mom would
be home alone in the morning before spending the rest of her day
shopping, bringing home the useless stuff she had begun to collect
and piling it up unopened in my brother's and my old bedrooms.

When I lived at home, Mom had washed her hairbrushes using
an old toothbrush to clean between the bristles, then let them dry
in the sun on a table in the backyard. She meticulously scrubbed
the grout between the kitchen tiles and polished her Revere ware
so the copper bottoms gleamed. She even ironed her sheets, pil-
lowcases, and Dad's boxer shorts. Now her house was dirty and
it smelled dirty.

I walked to the counter where the check lay and signed it,
saying to Mom, "Here's your money. You know this means you'll
never see us again." I had no other way to punish them for hurt-
ing me. "Say good-bye to your only grandchildren—part of that
money was for them." I turned to face her. "You know that this is
more than I borrowed." Her gaze was fixed on a spot on the wall.

I went into my old bedroom to retrieve a few personal items
I had left there. On my way to the front door I said, "I can't believe you forgave *that* man for strangling me, calling me those
foul names, the same ones he calls you. *That* man *abused* you and
cheated on you, and you take his side?"

I reminded her again of what she had told me when I asked
her for financial help.

"I never said that," she told me again.

"You, Mother, are a liar."

I stared at her for a few moments. She turned away. I walked
to the car, opened the trunk, and tossed in a couple of boxes. I
walked back to the front door. She hadn't moved.

"I cannot let either one of you around my girls," I told her.

She was looking at me now, but with no expression at all.

As I backed out of her driveway, I rolled down my window and said, with no small amount of satisfaction, "I now owe you nothing." Her mouth tightened into a pucker. I was again MIA. I remember thinking how much I loved the idea of never seeing them again. After all, what was there to miss?

We had never had family dinners. Mom's meals were usually some make-dinner-in-twenty-minutes recipe from a woman's magazine. The vegetables were boiled to mush and the meat was so overcooked I'd spit it into my napkin and flush it down the toilet when I got the chance. Her spaghetti sauce was a mix of canned tomato soup and mushroom soup ladled over watery noodles. The salads were a few slices of iceberg lettuce topped with mayonnaise.

When we lived in L.A., Dad worked second shift, so he was gone when Greg and I got home from school. Mom would fix us something from a box or the freezer, like a TV dinner, and we'd sit in front of the TV and eat in silence. Even when Dad wasn't working nights, we never sat at the table together sharing food and stories.

When we moved to the Bay Area, Mom and Dad ate dinner late, as they tended to their cocktail hour first. Mom would put something on the stove around six o'clock and at ten o'clock it would still be there, morphed into something unidentifiable. As soon as I got home from school I made sandwiches and took them to my room so I could eat them later when I got hungry.

The only time we had family dinners all sitting at the same table was on major holidays—and only if we had company—or when we were at someone else's house. There were no tender moments that tugged at my heart. Everything I liked about that house, Greg had put there.

He spent days and weeks and his own money putting up chair rails and wainscoting in his bedroom and in the family room. One whole wall of the living room had floor-to-ceiling, wall-to-wall bookcases that he designed and built. He refaced the living room fireplace with stone and a new wormwood mantel.

When I got a part-time job at JC Penney's, I bought deep scarlet carpeting for my bedroom. Greg spray painted the switch plate covers in the same color. I added scarlet curtains and painted the walls a soft white. Whatever was home about that house on Alderbrook Lane, the credit went to Greg. His projects were always generously and perfectly done and perfectly unappreciated.

One afternoon before my relationship with my parents ruptured, I stopped by their house, knowing that Greg would be there. He was done with his stint in the Navy and living there while he went back to school to complete his engineering degree. Mom and Dad had been on vacation, and Greg was putting up the wainscoting and painting the family room. We hung out until Mom and Dad pulled into the driveway.

I was anticipating what their reaction would be to Greg's fine work.

"What the hell is this?" Dad demanded. "Who said you could do this?" On and on he complained until Greg put his tools away and left, with me close behind. Later Mom told me she really liked what Greg had done, but I couldn't remember either Mom or Dad thanking Greg for all of his hard work.

Driving home after endorsing that equity check, I was so angry that my parents had taken money my daughters needed. I felt justified in telling Mom she would never see me or my kids again. I was done with my parents: their drinking, their hostilities, their name calling, their constant battles. When the girls and I had spent time at my parents' house and Dad got drunk, he called them names. He stared at them as they watched TV in the small family room and started slowly, criticizing small things at first: "Why are you wearing that ugly shirt?" Why is your hair so long?" "How come your shoe's untied?" Then the name calling would start in earnest.

A separation from my parents was long overdue. I needed a ceasefire.

Within a year, after a sudden violent encounter with my new hubby's fist following a daylong, drunken game of golf with several of our friends, my brief second marriage ended. "You stay away from me or I will press charges," I told him. I had now eighty-sixed three people from my life, four if I counted my first husband.

While I waited for my bruises to fade and my split lip to heal, I called a real estate agent. It took more than a year to sell the house; inflation was in double digits and the whole country was in recession. As soon as it sold I made arrangements with my employer to transfer to Oregon. California is a community property state, so even though my recent ex had contributed nothing to its purchase, I had to give him half the proceeds.

I was thirty-three years old and moving to Oregon, where I knew two people: my Uncle Cliff in Portland and one friend in Eugene. Between Portland and Eugene there is the small town of Corvallis, and it would be our new home. My daughters were twelve and nine. Recovering from the struggles and wounds I had suffered in California, all I could do was get out of bed each morning and go to work. The daily routine rendered me numb.

I didn't see my parents for almost six years.

Nine

During my early years in Oregon, I was haunted by my failures. I kept revisiting my past, especially high school, where I had felt so out of place. With the face we showed to the world our family had appeared normal. No one knew about Mom and Dad's late-night drinking or their wretched arguing. They got up early every morning and went to work, some days with painful hangovers. They paid their bills on time, took care of the house and yard, bought food, bought new cars, threw parties, went to parties, played golf. In the late 1950s they joined a small group of investors and cofounded a country club. No one could explain why their daughter had failing grades, or later on, two failed marriages.

Greg, in stark contrast, was good at everything. He was a straight-A student who had been invited to join Mensa. He hung out with the smart, nerdy crowd who went on to become engineers, doctors, and scientists. Mom and Dad never compared me to Greg, but I did, and I shouldn't have. One day when I asked Mom to stop her constant criticism she told me Greg was very disappointed in me. "He thinks you should have finished school," she said. "He says that it wasn't surprising that your marriages failed since you flunked out of college."

I believed her then because I believed it would be easy to be disappointed in me, to see me as the failure I felt I was. Not asking my brother how he felt, assuming Mom had told the truth, was a mistake. I had left for Oregon without telling Greg good-bye.

Many years later I found out he thought I had left without a word because I was no longer interested in him. Greg had become friends with my first husband and was a good friend of my second husband. It was my fault that I had failed so badly with both men, men Greg liked and seemed to approve of—or so Mom had told me. I would find our later that the same kind of whispering campaign she had used to criticize Dad had been, and would continue to be, used on me. At the time, it didn't really matter if I knew that or not. I couldn't remember the last time I myself had approved of anything I did.

Greg eventually sold his house, bought land, and built a forty-five-hundred-square-foot masterpiece. "It's what my architect calls a Frenchie," he explained. And French it was. Mansard roof, balconies, a grand entrance, gourmet kitchen, a third floor viewing room where you could see airports all the way from Reed Hillview to the south to San Francisco and Oakland to the north. Westward you could see the Permanente plant in Monte Vista across the wide Santa Clara Valley.

Neither Mom nor Dad understood what Greg was accomplishing as he poured his life into this house. It was soon selected as the most beautiful house in Milpitas. He truly loved the entire process of building his own home, though he was often interrupted by Mom and Dad's requests. He was about thirty minutes from their house, and any time they called he was there for them. He scraped leaves out of their rain gutters, tuned their cars, and changed their oil. He replaced water heaters and installed new dishwashers. He was right there for any reason to meet their needs as they grew older. My brother looked after them as much as he could, as much as he could stand—and more than they deserved. He was always paid with complaints.

When Dad's health began to fail, he mostly sat in his chair, no longer following Greg around to chat with him while he repaired, fixed, painted, or did whatever other task was at hand. The basic bones of the house always looked nice, with everything in good repair thanks to Greg. Eventually the whole place would be buried in hoarded merchandise, but from the outside no one would never guess.

One night Mom phoned him. "Greg! Our house is about to catch on fire!"

He rushed over to find that someone had turned off a wall switch that powered an outlet—that was all, no threat of fire. "I was not amused," he told me. "It was the middle of the night."

Eventually, Mom's constant bitching and her belittling of Dad drove Greg away. It got to the point where all he could do was attend to the chore at hand and then flee to the sanctuary of his home in the Milpitas hills.

Dad stayed closer and closer to home, only venturing out occasionally to golf. After a while no one included him in their twosomes or foursomes, and he eventually gave up playing the game he loved.

Meanwhile, Mom was out of the house all the time. She hunted newspaper ads for sales, and she bought and bought and bought. Her tastes were changing from fine antiques to pure junk, her real treasures becoming landfilled in the bedrooms as they filled up with plastic frogs from K-Mart and cheap blankets from Sears. She collected hundreds of sample bottles filled with shampoo, body washes, and lotions, none of them ever opened. Deposits of debris slowly buried the dust and filth that were accumulating in thick layers.

Ten

In 1981 I had a radical hysterectomy. My Pap smears had been in the mid-range for years, and my uterus was filled with fibroid tumors. In early 1982, I broke my foot attempting to play racquetball. In late 1982, I was rear-ended by a guy doing thirty-five. My car was totaled and so were my back and neck. In 1983 my bad luck turned to good when I met Douglas Edward Peck.

We dated for two months and then were married. He and my daughters became truly good friends. We bought a ranch-style house just outside the city limits of Corvallis. We had a half acre, a garden, a creek, tall trees, great kids, and good jobs. I had never felt so happy or so secure.

At my daughter's suggestion, we invited Mom and Dad to her high school graduation. I sent Mom a separate letter letting her know that if Dad didn't control his temper, they would be asked to leave. "My home is not like your place," I wrote as I closed my short letter.

My parents arrived at our house. I extended my hand to Dad and said, "Hi, Jim. Come in."

"Jim? What happened to Dad?"

"Okay then, Dad. Come on in. We have some things to snack on before Steph's graduation."

Mom asked to use the bathroom. As I led her down the hallway, she whispered, "He read your letter."

"What, Mom? Did you ask for the bathroom just for the chance to announce Dad's crimes? As I mentioned in that letter, this place is not like yours. You don't get to whisper here."

"That letter you sent about his having to behave himself. You addressed it to Mr. and Mrs. McRoberts, so he read it."

"Good. Then we all understand each other. Here's the bathroom."

At that moment, Steph came out of her bedroom. She was radiant. Her high school graduation had arrived. It had happened so fast. I hugged her and told her she looked beautiful.

Instead of proceeding into the bathroom, Mom started plucking at Steph's hair and pointing to her dress. "Is this what kids are wearing to graduation these days?"

"Mom," I said, "it would be a good idea if you kept up with what's fashionable for your granddaughters these days."

Too late. Steph was in tears and heading back to her bedroom. I whirled on my mother. "Good job, Mom. You could have at least said hello to her first."

"Well, I'm just saying that things must have changed with the younger set."

Dad, hearing our voices rising, joined us. "What's going on here?"

"Mom is about to excuse herself to the bathroom."

She walked in and closed the door. I turned and went to the kitchen to help Doug with the food. I quickly told him what had happened with Mom and Steph.

I herded my parents into the living room, set out food, then sat with them and launched into small talk. "How was your trip . . . ?"

Meanwhile, Doug knocked softly on Steph's door and asked her to help him with the champagne. Together they created a celebratory diversion by shaking up the bottles and shooting the corks off the edge of our deck.

Mom was not amused. "Hey, what are you doing with that champagne? I want some of that."

I surveyed the scene. It was too late. "Sorry, Mom," I said. "It's all gone. They were just having fun with it." She pursed her lips in disgust and drilled a hole in the floor with her eyes.

My daughter had already had enough of Mom and Dad. She would later recount the sting of Mom's scrutiny and her obvious disapproval of fun with champagne and tell me, "If I ever have another important event in my life, if I get married or have a kid, *those* people will *not* be invited."

We were all going to ride to the ceremonies in the same car, but Steph said, "I'm going to meet my friends. I'll see you after." I hugged her and handed her the corsage that went with her dress. The next time I saw her she was receiving her diploma. She looked confident and lovely, and my heart was filled with pride. After the ceremony I suggested we go to a nice restaurant in town instead of back to our house. Already, I was eager to send my parents on their way. The saving grace of the whole affair was that they were staying in a motel in town, not spending the night with us.

After Steph's graduation, I had little contact with my parents. Mom and I sent each other Christmas and birthday cards. Soon after graduating, Steph moved to Santa Cruz, California, and asked that I not let my parents know she was living so close. Doug sometimes went to the Bay Area on business and I accompanied him when I could to visit Steph. Once in a while we met Mom and Dad at their club for lunch or dinner, but usually we didn't let them know we were in town.

Three years after Steph graduated from high school, it was my youngest daughter, Kristen's, turn. We invited Mom and Dad to the ceremony. It would have been awkward to invite them to one graduation and not the other, but instead of asking them to our house we met them in town for a graduation dinner. Afterward, it would be quite some time before I saw them again.

When Kristen moved to the Bay Area two years later, she, too, asked that I not let her grandparents know she was living nearby. I kept both my daughters' secrets.

Eleven

Although distance from my parents had been good for me, I also lost contact with their relatives. I never knew what Mom had told her family about me, and fearing their rejection, I kept myself isolated from them. Besides, whenever I displeased Mom, she ordered me to stay away from them. "You *have* no grandparents, aunts, uncles, or cousins," she would say.

This punishment was meted out when I flunked out of college, when I became pregnant before I was married, and then again when I lived in sin. I began to see being disowned as a respite from her, and from the scrutiny of relatives she had lied to about me.

During the lengthy breaks in contact, most of Mom's family died. Her father passed away when I was in high school in the 1960s. In the mid-1980s her mother and her sister passed away. By the mid-1990s her youngest sister died. This devastated Mom; she had been close to all three of these lovely women. Dad's family also passed away. I had no idea where my first cousins were. From the few moments of contact I had with my grandparents, aunts, and uncles, I loved them all and always considered them to be truly nice people. Being frequently rejected from the family had given me much-needed breaks, but they came at a cost.

When Dad's parents died, he received nothing from their estate. Of course, his parents had acquired very little. Mom received a third of her parents' estate.

"Your father's family left him nothing," Mom would say, holding her thumb and fingers in the shape of a zero for emphasis. "I've put my mother's money in an account your dad can't get to." She also received many of my grandmother's possessions, those lovely things that are now in storage.

After my grandmother died I received a call from one of

Mom's sisters. It had been Grandma's wish that all six grandchildren pick out one item from her estate: Auntie Delores called to tell me she was shipping Grandma's old Singer sewing machine to me. We talked for a while, and then she said, "Karen, I've been thinking about you. Your mom sure is a bulldozer. That's about all I can say about her. All I can think is, poor Karen." Weirdly, I was elated to hear this. For the first time in my life I felt that someone else, someone who knew Lila O. Hanka McRoberts, saw through the Lila bullshit and understood what my life was like.

After Steph and Kris left home, I was finally back in school full time, taking up to twenty credits per term. I was so hungry for my college degree that I worked like a fool, earning a 4.0 GPA in most of my college courses.

In 1990, Mom had an aneurysm on her aorta and in late November had open heart surgery. Maybe it was because my own life was so wonderful by then that I was able to feel generous, put the past behind me, and get over the grudges and the hurt: I offered to spend my Christmas break at their house, cooking and cleaning while Mom mended. Dad could hardly boil water; his favorite snack was white bread crumbled into a drinking glass filled with milk and topped off with salt and pepper.

I made this offer to both of my parents, and both of them refused my help.

"Your father can put some frozen dinners in the microwave. That will be plenty for us."

I called again, letting them know I had five weeks off for Christmas break—the answer was no. I sent Mom a couple of get-well cards containing the same offer to stay with them and cook and clean. I received no reply.

Two years later when their golden anniversary rolled around, I received an invitation to join them at their country club. I wrote Mom a letter refusing the offer.

She made a rare phone call. "It won't look right if you're not there. I'll be embarrassed," she argued.

I've often wondered if not attending was the right decision. But I just couldn't bring myself to join such a celebration, and I explained why in a letter. I told her I had learned that marriage was about spending time together, holding hands, caring for each other. It wasn't about doing time and it wasn't about creating a war zone in your home.

"Convicted criminals do time in prison," I wrote. "Marriage is not about chalking up the years. In my opinion, your marriage is a cruel joke. It's like a black hole in outer space sucking the light and the life out of everything that comes near it. I cannot help you applaud that."

This was all true. Still, I'd like to think that at one time my parents had truly loved each other. Their wedding photo indicates love and happiness, hope. Their young faces shine with great expectations.

My daughters and brother went to the anniversary party, but I heard very little about it. Seven months later I called her to test the waters. We were planning another trip to the Bay Area, and I wasn't sure if I should stop by to see her or not.

"What do you want?" she said.

"Just to see how you guys are doing." Her long silence told me I was probably disowned again.

"You have no family. We are none of your business." She hung up the phone.

I was much more relieved than hurt. We would be free from her complaints and Dad's foul temper. Our trip would be a vacation without obligation.

Mercifully, Doug and I have a very different relationship from that of my parents. My childhood training didn't stick. Early on, Doug and I took the time to figure out how to argue so we didn't have to relive the same dead-end fight again and again. Over the span of our twenty-seven years together, I can count our big fights on one hand. We've discovered that they occur when there is an enormous amount of outside pressure on us—jobs, kids, trying to do too much in too little time. On every level we agree with each other: politics, religion, fidelity, financial management, family priorities, you name it.

We loved living outside the city limits. Each fall we cut our own firewood, splitting and stacking three cords for the winter months. We went skiing and camping. We spent five years remodeling our small house and landscaping the surrounding yard.

After living in our little house, then an empty nest, for thirteen years, we decided to sell it. We wanted to stay in the Corvallis area but wanted a more rural setting for our retirement. We bought forty-five acres and a house from hell came with them. When we weren't working on our tree farm or repairing the house, Doug and I took sailing classes and became certified captains, able to command vessels up to fifty feet in length. We traveled to Europe, went on wine tours, and drove many miles along I-5 to see my daughters in California.

I almost never thought about my parents and their house on Alderbrook Lane during that time. They were something I believed I had outgrown. I didn't miss the confusion and aggravation they brought into my life. Life itself no longer scared me, and I no longer made bad decisions based on fear, insecurities, or self-loathing. I had made my life my own.

Twelve

O ur new home was an adventure for us. Inside were filth and disrepair; the outside was trashed. The former owners had vandalized their own property, using it as their private garbage heap. The house reeked of cigarettes and animal waste. But there was nothing about the place that we couldn't clean up or fix up.

We hauled an amazing amount of trash and debris off the property, liberating the natural beauty that had been hidden by layers of garbage and neglect. In a row of blueberries Doug found half a waffle iron. He found an engine block from an old truck partially buried in the dirt. I found the bottom rack from a dishwasher hidden under piles of household trash grown over by blackberry vines. Everywhere there was brittle, decayed plastic and broken glass. We spent hours on our hands and knees picking up every offensive thing we could find.

Two weeks after we moved in, the place was clean enough to get new carpeting. When the installers arrived, we decided to take the half-mile walk to the mailbox and leave the guys alone to get started on the job. We were on our way out the door when the phone rang. It was Mom.

"Your dad's had a stroke, and he's in a nursing home," she said. "Hey, do you know anything about inheritance taxes?"

Mom wanted to know whether she would still be eligible for the five-hundred-thousand-dollar tax exemption from the sale of their home if Dad died. The San Jose tract house they had paid nineteen thousand dollars for in 1958 was now worth seven to eight hundred thousand dollars.

"The girls in my golf group tell me that after a spouse dies you shouldn't make any major decisions for a year," she continued. "I need to know if I can still get that tax exemption after your dad dies and I decide to stay in this house for the next year."

I recoiled at the obvious glee in her voice as she mulled the prospect of Dad's death—something she had long wished for aloud—and the cold calculation behind her phone call to me. Nowhere was there concern about how the news of Dad's stroke might affect me.

"Mom, when did Dad have this stroke and where is he now?"

"Oh, about a week ago. He's been released from the hospital and he's in a nursing home."

After that, Mom started calling me daily with a litany of complaints.

"Your dad calls me about every hour asking me to bring him home. It's driving me nuts. How does he get to a phone if he's bedridden?"

I speculated that he was using the phone at the nurse's station. I should have told her that her calls were driving *me* nuts, but I kept quiet and let her rant.

During one call I returned to a suggestion I'd made before, that she leave Dad. "Maybe you should see a lawyer and file for divorce. It's clear you don't want him home, and you don't want to share your assets with him. But California is a community property state, so the most you can get is half of what you guys own. If you're still married, you might even have to give him half of what you inherited from your mom."

She had good reasons to leave him, her obvious loathing for him being only one. She was tiny, and while Dad was not a big guy, his anger made him seem huge, and once in a while he'd shove her around. When in a rage, his lips became thin white strips and his eyes glared without blinking.

He had once broken his brother's ribs. This brother had a serious drinking problem, and one time he came into a tavern in Ketchum where Dad was bartending. He was either embarrassingly drunk already or trying to bum a drink. Dad reached across the bar, grabbed his shirtfront, and slammed his brother's torso against the bar with such force that he broke several bones. Mom had to rush her brother-in-law to the hospital. When pumped full of anger-fueled adrenaline, Dad could easily leap over the bar to break up a fight. His anger robbed him of reason and any thought of consequences.

Mom knew this, yet remained the most frequent provoker of his nasty temper. Dad usually retaliated in kind, matching her one-for-one in nasty verbal slams.

The calls continued, always difficult to receive. "How's Dad doing?" I would ask.

Her answers were always some variation of "He's made of iron, tough as old shoe leather. If he had any decency he would just die."

Within a couple of weeks, Dad was home and my parents' life returned to its chaotic and unstable state. Mom's calls became irregular and short.

"Have to go. *He's* listening," she'd say as she hung up.

Doug and I both worked four ten-hour days a week so we could have three-day weekends. Since we lived so far out of town, this schedule saved us one long commute per week. It also offered us the opportunity to leave late on a Thursday afternoon to have a long weekend at the coast and not worry about getting home until late Sunday evening.

Another way I took advantage of my three-day weekends was to head south to visit my parents and my daughters. My youngest daughter, Kristen, lived in Palo Alto, not too far from their house. I usually flew to San Jose Airport and she picked me up. She would drop me at her grandparents' on her way to work.

Mom was always anxious to get away from Dad, so she'd hand me her car keys and we'd go to antique shops or over to one of her friends' houses, not getting back to Alderbrook Lane until late in the afternoon when Kristen would drive by and pick me up. Then my daughter and I would go out to dinner, and I'd spend the evening telling her about my discoveries at Mom and Dad's house.

I can't pinpoint when Mom started what she called "collecting." It was hoarding. The clutter drove me nuts. Doug and I kept our house clean and organized; we both hated wasting time looking for something that should be in a known place.

When I asked her about it she'd complain that she couldn't get anything done with Dad sitting on his ass all day long and getting in her way. But he spent most of his days snoozing on his recliner while TV blared out a golf game. He was anything but in the way.

When Dad was awake and wanting his first drink of the day, Mom would consent to be in the same room with him. Strange how things could change between them, what chameleons they could become with one another. When they were compatible— when Mom wasn't pushing buttons and Dad wasn't in a rage— she and Dad were a solidified unit. During these calm periods of solidarity, they focused their joint attention on whoever was available. When I was at their house, I became the object of their scrutiny.

Was I gaining weight? Did I really like my hair that curly and long? Why was I driving a Toyota—didn't I used to have a Ford? Why did I take the side of minorities when minorities were such losers? Questions such as these always put me on the defensive. I fought the urge to come out swinging with harsh words of my own to stop them cold, to put them in their place, to assert myself. Most of the time, a better plan was to keep quiet until they either ran out of steam or got so loaded that they devolved into babbling.

Thirteen

During the next couple of years Dad had several more strokes. Each time he recovered and went home. And each time Mom was livid. She enjoyed having the house to herself, her life to herself. With him home she found ways to make his life edgy.

He quit smoking but still demanded his evening drinks. Along with her first drink of the day, she would light a cigarette and blow smoke his way, taunting him with what he could no longer have.

Fortunately the strokes hadn't paralyzed him, but Mom told me he was falling a lot, and he complained of back pain. She was worried that she would end up like her mother, caring for an invalid for as long as he lived. When I learned he'd been falling, I suggested she take him to his doctor so his health could be monitored more carefully. As usual, she ignored me.

"The old boy is so tough that he'll outlive all of us. He's always fine, always fine ..."

Dad was also being treated for skin cancer. His fair Irish skin, exposed to full sun while he skied, golfed, and went bareheaded through the years, was starting to rebel. He had dozens of melanomas removed, and his face was becoming crosshatched with scar tissue.

Dad had worked on the Gemini and Apollo space projects for Lockheed Missiles and Space. I remember a time when he returned from a rocket launching at Cape Canaveral, Florida. He was so sunburned that he could peel a sheet of skin off his shin in one continuous piece. His ears peeled for days and days, the skin flaking onto his shoulders like dandruff.

Dad's return to good health after his strokes didn't last too much longer. In 1999 he was supposed to be driving to his primary physician's for a checkup when his dermatologist's office called Mom.

"Mrs. McRoberts, your husband is here but he has no appointment scheduled for today. He seems confused. You should probably pick him up. He can't remember where he parked his car."

Dad had been involved in a minor fender bender and, after exchanging insurance information with the person whose car he bumped into, had left his car at the curb. He had walked from there to the dermatologist's office.

Mom went to pick him up. "We had to drive up and down every street in Mountain View looking for his damned car. And then I had to tail him home, hoping that he could find his way. He wouldn't let me lead him. He had to be in front. You have no idea how this interrupted my day. I thought I'd never get home."

Dad received a citation for the fender bender, and there was a small insurance claim from the driver he had hit. It was at this point that his doctor told him he had to give up his driver's license.

He was heartbroken when he had to exchange the license for a California ID card. He knew it was necessary, but he grieved his loss of freedom.

Mom called again. "You will never believe what that bastard did last night. He still insists on sleeping in the nude, and that's not a pretty sight. He got up in the middle of the night and sat in his car with his bare butt on the upholstery I have to sit on—and he has hemorrhoids—and he cried like a baby. I tried to get him back into bed, but he wouldn't budge, so I tossed him a blanket and left him there in the cold garage. Can you believe that? I would have been humiliated if any of the neighbors saw that. I hope no one heard him."

"Mom, Dad's losing everything. Go easy on him."

"Go easy on *him?* Who goes easy on me?"

"Mom, look at you. You're still strong. You can walk without falling and you can dress yourself and drive a car and run a vacuum cleaner and make decisions. Dad used to golf anytime he wanted to. Now he doesn't go anywhere. He's dependent on you now, so go easy on him."

This advice was met with silence.

"Mom, there are so many places we can go to find help for Dad, and that will help *you*. People can come to your house to take care of him and take the burden off you. You can hire in-home care for him and a housekeeping service for yourself."

Apparently this was not advice she wanted to hear either. She hung up on me, and I didn't hear from her for a little while.

And then she started calling me again.

"Now I have to be his chauffeur. He wants to golf. He can hardly stand up, let alone swing a club. His demands interfere with *my* nine-hole group. I never get anything done these days."

Reasoning was no help at all.

"He's on the couch again. I can hardly stand this. Sleep, all he does is sleep."

"Mom, go out. Get in your car and go somewhere. Consider it a break. He can't make demands on you if he's sleeping."

There was no talking sense to her.

During the next couple of years Dad developed congestive heart failure. Fluids pooled in his lungs. His chest rattled and his feet swelled like balloons, making it painful to walk as he shuffled along.

"He's always falling. It's just like a tree in the forest. He hits the floor like a falling log," Mom complained. "He has lumps all over his skull. I can hardly stand to look at him. And he's starting to tilt sideways when he walks. He needs a walker but won't use one. I won't take him anywhere. He embarrasses me."

I started seeing my parents more frequently. It wasn't comfortable, but my own good life had made it easier to be generous. And since they had alienated my brother, I figured it was my turn to help.

As soon as I entered the house one day, Mom tugged my arm. "I have something to show you down in the bedroom."

I followed her.

"Oh, he's such a bastard. You don't know what I put up with." She started listing Dad's crimes: he was on the couch, he spilled his coffee, he fell, he hit his head again, he peed on the couch, he wandered in his sleep, the TV was too loud, he never left his chair, his nose ran, he had tumors on his face, he sat in his car and cried, he, he, he …

I waited for her to take a breath.

"No one comes to see us anymore, and I can't get anything done."

By this time, my parents' house had become a nightmare. Their beautiful furniture had disappeared under piles of shopping bags, rumpled laundry, junk mail, catalogs, soiled clothing, and an amazing array of pure junk she had found on sale somewhere. The very walls were disappearing behind the rubble as she piled up towels from Mervyn's, quilts from Macy's, clocks, bric-a-brac, and tchotchkes from K-Mart and stacked them along the baseboards. This served as a foundation for more shopping bags filled with Christmas ornaments and stuffed Easter bunnies. My old bedroom, Greg's old bedroom, the living room, the family room, and the sunroom were filled with so much stuff that there was only enough space to enter the room, turn around, and exit the way you had come in. Of course, she blamed the mess on Dad.

"I can't get a damn thing done with him around. He spends all day on the couch. And he's having *accidents*. I am so embarrassed for him."

"Mom, you should take him to the doctor."

"Nah, he's tough as nails."

She bought toilet paper every time she went to the store. "He needs a lot of this to clean up his messes," she told me. "I'm spending all of my retirement wiping his bum."

It was escape from Dad that continually sent her into the aisles of the hundreds of stores that clogged the Bay Area. Her house became her own private garbage dump.

I could not seem to resist attempting reason, no matter how often I was rebuffed. "You know, Mom, you're the one hauling in all this stuff. If you'd stop shopping and spend some time cleaning there would be no mess."

"Why should I do all the work while that bastard sleeps away his days?"

I started trying to help her with efficiency during my brief visits.

"Mom, look. Here's a dirty glass that you put in the sink this morning. With the same amount of energy and time you could have put it in the dishwasher. Done!"

I tried to convince her that junk mail was dangerous, harmful to the environment, and fodder for the landfills. "It will take years to get you off all of these lists. Identity theft can happen to you because you're on so many."

"I love getting mail. *Him* gets no mail at all."

Fourteen

My mother-in-law, Harriett Peck, passed away in 1996 following surgery to repair her gallbladder. She died in the hospital. Afterward we learned there had been no funeral plans made prior to her death; my in-laws were healthy and didn't anticipate a funeral so early in their lives. My husband and his father got through the ordeal somehow, though the grief was nearly unbearable. My in-laws' marriage was so unlike my parents'. They were *Ozzie and Harriet, Father Knows Best, Leave it to Beaver,* and *The Donna Reed Show* all rolled into one.

Harriett's sudden death prompted me to ask my parents about their afterlife care. Mom told me she and dad had bought plots in a Catholic cemetery in Los Altos Hills.

"You're a Lutheran and Dad's an atheist—how did you guys get a place to rest in a Catholic cemetery?" I asked.

"We just paid their price and signed their forms," she replied.

In spring of 2002, I drove to California to see my daughters. I also planned to see my parents and Mom wanted us to go antique shopping with her friend Bev. We perused the shops along San Carlos Street and then went over to Los Altos where there was an antique store Bev wanted to visit. As we traveled along Foothill Boulevard, Mom mentioned that we were close to the cemetery. Bev had also made plans to be interred there in the mausoleum and said that if we didn't mind stopping there, she had some business to take care of in the office.

While Bev was in the admin building I asked Mom to show me where her and Dad's plots were.

We walked down the hill toward the burial grounds. I heard the sound of a lawnmower in the distance. It was late afternoon, glorious spring weather with a gentle breeze tickling my hair against my cheek.

My mother's face was partially shaded by a small linden tree.

She looked soft and small. As we stood looking down at where her body would lie, I wondered what she might be thinking or feeling while she pondered her fate. I watched her as she gazed at the ground where she and Dad would be forever. I couldn't imagine what it was like to stand above your final resting place.

Mom nudged me with her elbow. I was hoping she would say something profound, something I could keep with me as I aged and got to the same place in my life.

"You know, your father has been such a bastard. If he dies first, I think I'll have him cremated. That way I can save about five or six thousand dollars on funeral expenses."

"What?"

"I don't want to be buried with that bastard for all eternity. I want to be over there in the mausoleum with Bev."

Fifteen

Once upon a time, Mom's home had been lovely, beautiful enough to be photographed for a magazine. It was clean and orderly, beautifully appointed. A professional interior decorator helped Mom make her selections, choosing just the right accessories, upholstery, carpeting, and drapes.

Now it was starting to smell. There was no place to sit. Dad had had several accidents while napping on the couch, so it was now covered with brightly colored beach towels. Every surface was sticky or smudged. All of the plastic light switches and their covers were coated with a dark residue of grime. In the kitchen sink the sponge and dishrag smelled like mildew. I wanted to wash my hands the entire time I was there.

My brother had long since given up helping our parents, beyond what was absolutely necessary, and that included helping Mom make better decisions.

He had offered the same advice I had—hire someone to help—but she absorbed none of it. She could only hear what she wanted to hear. He, too, had witnessed the accumulation of clutter and dirt and had found no way to intervene. "It's like talking to a brick," he told me.

In 2003, Mom called and asked me to come down to clean out their garage. "It's getting so bad I can't get both cars into it," she said.

"Mom, Dad can no longer drive. Why do you have two cars?"

"I keep one as a spare, just in case."

There was no point in asking, in case of what?

This time there was no room at all in any of my parents' spare bedrooms, so I stayed with Kristen, who picked me up at the airport. The next morning, a Friday, she dropped me off at the house on her way to work, saying, "Mom, if anything goes wrong here today, call me on my cell. I can leave work at any time to come and get you." I hugged her good-bye and we gave each other a thumbs-up.

"I'll be back to pick you up around four thirty," she said.

I had to grin at her concern, but I, too, was worried about how my day would play out.

Mom and Dad were just getting up. Dad was making coffee and Mom was pouring out prescription pills into two piles. Mom noticed my raised eyebrows as I stared at the piles of medications.

"These are my pills for the day, and those are your father's," she explained.

I picked up a couple of bottles and looked at their labels.

"Mom," I said. "This one in Dad's pile is phenobarbital. And in the same pile you have an Ambien. Are you sure he should be taking both?"

"Oh, he knows how to take his meds."

No wonder Dad slept all day. I sighed and said, "OK." I went into the garage and flipped on the light switch. The garage remained dark. I pressed the garage door opener to let in some extra light, but it wasn't much help. I could see that the cars were both there, but parked so closely one had to be moved out in order to open the door to the other. I had no idea how my elderly mother had been able to navigate these cars in and out of her garage. She could barely see over the steering wheel.

I parked the cars at the curb and then went back into the garage. I had no idea where to start. The only empty space was where the cars had been. Everywhere else there was stuff, piled up high against the walls. My job for the day was triage, sort things into recycle, donate, trash, so when Kristen and I came back together the next day we'd have it all figured out. By the end of the day we'd be done and then off to drinks and dinner at some posh place in downtown Palo Alto to enjoy our time together.

I walked to a spot where I thought I could start, but then I noticed something: pill vials, everywhere. I picked one up. Its label had been peeled off. I opened it. Inside the capped vial was a dead insect. I grabbed another one; same thing, label peeled, dead insect inside. *What the hell?* I followed a trail of pill vials out the side door and into the backyard. The little brown plastic bug coffins were all over the place: under the grapefruit tree, near the rose bushes, dotted under the clothesline, and scattered along the fences. Mom's obsessive fear of insects must have taken an even more neurotic twist.

I went back to the garage and contemplated the filth around me. I drove one of Mom's cars to Home Depot and bought gloves, dust masks, heavy-duty contractor's garbage bags, and several bottles of water. Back at Mom's place, the garage looked no friendlier for the fact I was now armed with grime-fighting materials.

I decided to start at the highest spot and work my way down. I set up their rickety wooden ladder and pulled cardboard boxes down from the rafters. Most of them had been there since the late 1950s. Each of them was in a plastic bag with a twist tie closure that was covered with dust and muck and they were all empty. They had once contained brand new items Mom had long since disposed of: a blender, an electric frying pan, a set of dishes, a crock pot.

"All these empty boxes hogging space that could be used for the stuff piled up against the walls," I muttered to myself. But then I realized that neither Mom nor Dad could manage to climb a ladder anymore.

I flattened the cardboard for recycling and set up a garbage bag for trash. By midmorning I felt scummy, covered with fall-out from the high shelves. I shook my hair in the sunlight and watched debris swirl away and fall to the ground.

The wall shelves were covered with toxic pollutants collected over the past forty-five years, pesticides, old paint, household cleaners, and dozens of brown glass chemical bottles with no labels on them. A trail of these extended into the backyard. I decided later would be a good time to deal with those. By noon I was exhausted, unable to make any decisions at all. My chest wheezed and my eyes itched.

Mom peeked out every once in a while to see how I was doing. The first time, she said "This is kind of fun, eh? Going through all this old stuff."

"No, Mom, it's not fun at all. It's hot and miserable, and it's apparent that no one has taken care of *her* stuff in more than four decades."

"Don't throw out anything I want to keep," she admonished.

Add mind reader to my chores. Just what I needed, another task of sleuthing what to keep and what to ditch.

By the end of the day I had sorted only the items on the top shelf. Kristen arrived and I pulled Mom's cars into the driveway and closed the garage door.

Mom wasn't pleased. "Are you sure you can't put the cars in the garage? This neighborhood is no longer safe. The Asians are filling up the place. I don't feel secure anymore."

Kristen and I both chided her over this comment.

"Gramma, anyone who can pay eight or nine hundred thousand dollars for one of these places is not about to trash your neighborhood or steal one of your old cars."

It wasn't hard to see Mom's comment coming. Several years earlier, the neighborhood had had a huge problem with squirrels; the old fruit trees attracted them. One day a squirrel came into contact with a transformer and was electrocuted. The poor creature fell into my parents' backyard. Dad picked up the little thing with a shovel, intending to put it into the garbage can that was already out at the curb ready for the next day's pickup.

The little suffering animal's hair had all been singed off and its long slender tail was devoid of fur, giving it a rat-like appearance. Still alive, it wriggled off Dad's shovel and writhed on the sidewalk. A Chinese lady who lived across the street was also putting trash in her garbage can at curbside. She saw Dad with the shovel and the squirrel with no fur twisting on the sidewalk.

"Rats!" she yelled. "Kill it! Smash it with your shovel! You have rats!" she screamed at Dad and ran into her house.

Mom was furious. "How dare she accuse me of having rats? She came from a country *famous* for its abundance of rats."

From that day forward, on and on Mom would go about the Asian invasion. When I reminded her that she liked the couple from India who lived next door and that one of her golfing partners was from Japan, she said, "Well, I like the Asians at our club and our neighbors are doctors, but the rest of them are not my cup of tea. They don't speak English in the grocery stores."

"Mom, may I remind you that you did not speak English until you were six years old and had to go to public school?" She *still* spoke some Finnish phrases when she was trying to hide conversations from Dad.

"They are just so rude to be chattering away like that in the stores," she said. "No one can understand them."

"Mom, they're having a private conversation, and what they're talking about is none of your business. And anyway, maybe you should stop shopping for a while until we can sort all this stuff out."

A wave of her hand shut me up. And she was right; it was a waste of breath to try to reason with her.

Sixteen

I took a very long, very hot shower at Kristen's apartment and we went out to dinner. It felt so normal to be with her after the chaos at Mom's place. We shared a bottle of wine and talked about her work and my work, our lives, politics, the environment. We enjoyed our meal and walked back to her apartment in the cool of a California evening.

Kristen had generously offered to help me finish cleaning the garage, sacrificing her weekend freedom. I tried to offer a few words of warning as we approached the house early Saturday morning. She was armed with coffee and I had my orange juice: we were as ready as we could get. We agreed that we should try to keep Mom in the house as much as possible.

We decided to start at the back of the garage and work our way to the front. We opened every cabinet and put the contents on the floor. Then we organized everything in three piles as planned: trash, recycle, or donate.

We came to the part of the garage that was truly scary and that we knew would take some time, the toxic waste dump portion of the estate, which included chemicals long since banned. Kristen had scheduled a drop-off at a hazardous waste collection site in Santa Clara; our appointment was for eleven o'clock.

"Geez, Mom," Kristen said as she surveyed the mess, "if Grampa were to stumble and fall into some of this stuff it could be really toxic. One elbow near that shelf and—ka-boom."

"Yup," was all I could say.

We found a cardboard box that would fit into the trunk of her car. We lined it with a plastic tarp and put in it plastic bags filled with every toxic substance we could find, labeled and un-labeled. If Mom or Dad needed paint, they could hire a painter. At their ages they had no business getting up on ladders and juggling paint trays anyway. They had a gardener, so they no longer needed poisons for the yard.

Every once in a while Kris or I made trips inside to use the bathroom. Along the way we kept our eyes peeled for obvious items we could take to the hazmat center. Under Mom's kitchen sink there were old cans of insecticides, air fresheners that emitted high doses of formaldehyde and benzene, and old detergents that contained phosphates. We smuggled these items out to the box in Kris's car. In the bathrooms I found a lot of over-the-counter medicines that were dated five, seven, ten years ago, some not dated at all—prescriptions filled before labeling laws were enacted. Pretending to look for a snack, Kristen found old food in the kitchen and put that in a large garbage bag in the garage as well.

Mom came out to the garage just as we were putting all the pesticides in the box.

"I paid good money for those!" she wailed. Then, "You can't get rid of *that* one. I use it!"

"Mom, most of these pesticides are banned. They're too toxic to use."

"I don't care. I hate insects and they need to be killed."

"Gramma, you're polluting my world," Kristen said. "If I ever have kids, your chemicals will make them sick."

"I don't care. I paid for these products and they're mine."

"Mom, you don't need this stuff. Just stop providing insects and mice with places to nest, and you won't need anything so poisonous," I said.

I picked up an old newspaper and put several sheets on the garage floor. "See, Mom, you put these papers down and bugs crawl into them, earwigs and such. They like to hide. So you either need to dance around on the paper every morning, or just stop inviting them here."

She wasn't listening. She had started for Kristen's car, determined to retrieve her precious chemicals.

"Mom, please. Everything there has been banned for good reasons. This poison is toxic for all of us. If you don't want insects and pests, *stop making nests for them.*"

She continued down the driveway. I followed.

"Mom, I can show you dozens of methods to get rid of insects that aren't dangerous. Just cleaning up this mess will help a lot."

"Leave it alone! I'll just buy more after you guys are gone," she threatened.

"Yeah?" Kristen said, advancing on Mom. "They don't sell this stuff anymore, so good luck with that."

Then I watched as my daughter wrapped her arms around Mom's torso, pinning her arms to her sides, and hauled her back to the house. Kristen rarely lost her temper, but Mom's callous remarks about polluting Kristen's future had pushed some buttons.

"Gramma," she said as she wrestled her toward the house, "if you come out here again, we're leaving. You'll have this huge mess on your hands and we'll be gone. And no one will put your cars away!"

Dad peeked out of the door. "What's going on out here?"

"Grandpa, your wife is causing problems," Kristen answered. "Best to keep her in the house."

"Lila!" Dad yelled at Mom as she stomped back into the house.

Kris and I used the next hour to fill the boxes in her car with as many toxic items as we could find, then left on our mission. The stench leaking out of the trunk was so powerful we had to drive to the hazmat place with all windows rolled down and we still felt nauseous.

We managed to get to the place on time. It looked like Armageddon—everyone dressed in ominous white suits. A masked face appeared at Kristen's window. "Do not get out of your car," a voice said, "just open the trunk."

More white suits removed Mom's precious inventory from the trunk. They took out all of the solvents, the old paint, the pesticides, the unidentifiable items, the lead fishing weights I had found, the old leaking batteries, the canned food with puffy lids, the old medications. They also took the plastic tarp and the cardboard box.

Kristen's car still reeked as we drove to a Salvation Army collection truck. There we offloaded two more boxes from her backseat that were filled with donations, Dad's old fishing gear, small appliances never opened or used.

At the nearby Safeway we washed our hands and then washed them again. We ordered sandwiches and drinks from the deli and drove to Calabasas Park. We sat on the baseball bleachers and ate in silence.

Across the field near the recreation center was a large group of women doing tai chi exercises. They were all elderly, graceful, and strong.

"Why can't Gramma get involved with stuff like that?" Kristen said. "It would get her out of the house, away from Grandpa, help her stay healthy. I just don't get her."

"Join the club."

When we returned to the garage, we found Mom picking through the bags we had carefully filled with sorted items. She had obliterated our organization scheme while we were gone.

Once again, Kristen demanded that Mom return to the house.

As we uncovered the walls of the garage we found a collection of more than two hundred rolls of toilet paper stashed in a corner. As we pulled them free we were assaulted by the strong odor of rodents. We put on our dust masks, pulled on rubber gloves, and moved in to examine the area. It was clear we had an infestation of mice on our hands and it reeked. Just then, Mom came out again, making the lame excuse that she needed something from the garage fridge.

"You're not going to throw that out!" she said when she saw the piles of filthy toilet paper. "I got all of that on sale."

Again Dad peeked out the door. "What the hell is going on?"

"Nothing, Dad. Just a little discussion with Mom about sanitation. She's coming back inside."

Reluctantly, Mom went back into the house, her hands clenched and her shoulders up around her ears.

By then it was late in the afternoon and we still had about half the garage left to sort through and clean. Mom continued to appear.

I was losing patience. "Mom, you made this mess and you called us to help you clean it up. Let's face it, you obviously cannot stop buying things, and you're no longer capable of keeping your house clean. Now leave us alone or we'll leave and call the health department. You're endangering your health and ours."

"Gramma," said Kris, "you cannot possibly think about using this nasty toilet paper on your private parts."

"Your father has *accidents*. You have no idea what I have to clean up," she said. "I need that toilet paper. His messes are so foul. All I do all day long is wipe his bum."

Dad returned to the door to ask what all the noise was about. When Kristen moved toward him to explain, Mom retreated.

I had put Dad's old tool chest in a donation pile. The tools were old and rusted, and Dad's shaky hands could no longer hold a screwdriver or pound a nail. Greg always brought his own tools when he worked on Mom and Dad's house.

"Don't get rid of that," Dad said. "I need it for work tomorrow." Then he shuffled back to his recliner. He had retired almost thirty years earlier.

Kristen and I continued to sort, clean, organize, and sort and clean some more. We found a two-year supply of coffee, the cans' lids coated with dust, more toilet paper, almost a hundred cans of soup, more than fifty light bulbs, and more batteries than we had time to count. We found plastic packages of candied fruits. At least that's what the packages said; the contents were black, gooey, and unidentifiable.

"Geez," said Kristen. "I never knew candied fruit could go bad."

There were golf balls everywhere packed in one- and two-dozen egg cartons held together with rubber bands. Buried under five feet of magazines, newspapers, boxes of old moldy golf shoes, and frayed towels there was my great aunt Amelia's sewing machine, which she inherited when Amelia passed away. It was a White in beautiful condition.

The old machine triggered many memories. "You know, the few times I visited Mom's family in Minnesota, I learned things. Great Aunt Amelia and Grandma Ida taught me how to sew on their old machines. I was in such a hurry to make clothes that I made my first dress completely inside out."

Kristen nudged me. "Stop reciting family history. Let's get this over with today so we can have Sunday to ourselves and won't have to come back here."

Mom had a shop vacuum that we used to suck up spider webs, broken golf tees, dust and dryer lint, many, many twist ties, and more dirt. One small mercy: my brother took excellent care of their cars, so there were no greasy motor oil messes on the cement.

As daylight became scarce we worked harder, stuffing Kristen's car with bags and bags of trash, recyclables, and donations.

When at last we finished, we drove the cars into the garage.

Dad came to the door again. "Why don't you girls come in and have a drink with me?"

"We're so dirty," I said. "We're going to head back to Kristen's and shower. I have a flight out tomorrow and want to go to bed early. But thanks for the offer, Dad."

Dad's strokes seemed to have calmed down his foul temper. I knew he still flared up around Mom, but to the rest of us he was pleasant now, even sweet.

"You didn't get rid of my toolbox, did you? I need it for work tomorrow," Dad repeated.

He had been showing signs of stroke-related dementia for several years. Sometimes he caught himself; sometimes he didn't. We never bothered to correct him.

"No, Dad," I lied. "All of your things are OK."

Mom joined him at the door. "Hey, Mom," I said. "Please try to keep this clean."

She nodded her head and tried to look happy. She thanked us, which took me by surprise. On her way into the house, she wrestled a large jug of Carlo Rossi wine through the door. Dad disappeared into the house. Kris and I drove away and the garage door slowly closed behind us.

We dropped off the remaining donations at the same Salvation Army truck. We went to the landfill in Palo Alto and dropped off the recyclable items and the rest of the trash. We showered and went to a Thai place for dinner.

We both felt bewildered. "I'm ready for a shrink's couch," I said.

For an entire hour we couldn't talk about anything but what we had seen that day; we tried moving on to other subjects, but we simply couldn't.

"Hey," Kristen said, "did you see the rest of the house?"

"Yeah." I felt myself tearing up as I picked at my shrimp and sipped my wine.

As we ate and talked, we believed the garage was behind us now. We thought Mom would like the organization and cleanliness and that it would motivate her to clean the rest of her house.

Little did we know.

Seventeen

In 2004, Mom was eighty-six and Dad was ninety. They had lived in their house on Alderbrook Lane since 1958. Dad had his stroke-related vascular dementia, congestive heart failure, and an epidemic of skin cancers. He couldn't lift his legs to climb a single step, and he was losing both his eyesight and his hearing. He was also plagued with osteoporosis, as was Mom. He was curling into a question mark. Mom was straight as a stick, but she was shrinking; her severe bone disease made her brittle as could be, like an old China teacup. Mom also had congestive heart failure and a second aneurysm on her aorta, and she was having major dental problems.

"We're buying a brand new house in St. George, Utah," Mom announced on the phone.

I had no idea where that was.

"It's a new development. Margaret and Chuck live there. We're going to live near them."

Margaret and Chuck Higgins were fantastic people. Mom and Dad had met them in Ketchum, and they had all lived in Reseda at the same time. They were a bit younger than my parents, but not by much. These old friends had kept in touch once in a while by phone or Christmas card, but they hadn't seen each other in years.

It was a spur-of-the-moment phone call that had sparked my parents' interest in going to Utah. Apparently, Dad was quite lucid when he talked to Chuck; it sparked some old memories. Chuck was a talker: smart, funny, and charming. Margaret was beautiful and sweet, always loving, with the ability to make anyone feel comfortable. Mom got the idea that Dad would be better off in Chuck's company. While she had no indication from the two old friends that this would be true, she accepted it as fact.

I wrote Mom a five-page letter begging her not to move. I

asked her to consider in-home nursing care for Dad, a cleaning service, an assisted living facility. I knew she hated "wiping the ol' boy's bum" and pointed out that she wouldn't have to if she consented to having professionals help her with him.

I promised I would come down more often. I pointed out that Kristen was only thirty minutes away from them. Greg, forty minutes. Stephanie was three hours away in the Sierra Nevadas. If Doug and I pushed it, we could drive there in ten hours.

Hearing nothing, I called her to plead my case. "Mom, Utah is way the hell away. It's a place we will never visit—no one in the family is interested in lizard land. You'll have no family, no doctors, no dentists, nothing. Just get some home nursing care and assisted living for Dad and he won't be such a burden to you."

"I won't spend one dime on that bastard. And I will not have strangers in my house."

"Mom, face it. You're both too old for this."

"I will not have strangers in my house," she repeated. "They'll see how much we have and they'll rob us. They'll steal everything."

"Mom, a move like this at your age is crazy!"

"Stop trying to sabotage my happiness!" She hung up.

Greg tried too, bringing up the same issues that I had. And he pointed out that even a new house demands a lot of work and there would be no one there to help them. He finally told her that if she didn't carefully reconsider her decision, he was through trying to persuade her. If she wouldn't even consider his arguments, all he could do was wish her luck.

The phone rang. "Your brother wished us luck. He said he was happy for us. I wish you could do the same."

Eighteen

Neither Greg nor I held sway. Mom hired her realtor's husband to renovate their outdated kitchen. She contracted her gardener to landscape the front yard. The house in Utah wasn't even built yet; it wouldn't be available for four or five months. Mom proceeded with her plans.

It was clear I couldn't stand in her way, but maybe I could at least protect her as she prepared to leave.

"Mom, it seems to me that there's a conflict of interest. You hired your realtor's husband to do the kitchen."

"Yes, I did. He's Finnish."

"That's beside the point. You've had no bids. No other contractors have offered their advice or opinions. What if he does a lousy job, or does things that aren't even necessary? He's working for his wife, not for you or Dad—he'll do whatever she tells him to do and you'll pay him . . . them. You have no paperwork, no agreement. You don't even know if he's licensed or insured."

Her eyes went blank, as they often did when she dismissed me. It signaled she was finished with the subject.

"How are you paying for all of this?"

"We have a reverse mortgage," Mom said. "So far we've gotten twenty-seven thousand dollars. We were qualified for a hundred thousand."

All I could say to that was, "Great."

In September Mom and Dad flew from San Jose to Las Vegas. They had no cell phones, so when they arrived in Vegas they had no way to contact Margaret and Chuck, who had driven more than two hours from St. George to pick them up.

Chuck was hanging around the luggage carousel, hoping to find Mom and Dad by process of elimination. But it had been many years since these two couples had seen each other. Mom and Dad had changed so much.

"I would not have recognized your parents," Chuck told me later. "It was your mother who spotted us."

Chuck and Margaret lived in phase one of the Coral Canyon development in Washington, Utah, about thirty minutes outside St. George. Phase two was just beginning. Chuck took Mom and Dad to the sales office, where they picked out their floor plan, carpet colors, tile, exterior, and location. They picked a house that was just seven houses away from Margaret and Chuck's. I felt a little better knowing that their friends would be close.

Mom was very excited about her new house. She signed all the documents, making it official. Dad signed too, although legal scrutiny would have rendered his participation null and void on account of his dementia. Mom had a couple of transient ischemic attacks (TIAs—mini-strokes) on her health record, but nothing else in her medical history indicated she wasn't competent to make sound decisions. The house was supposed to be ready in late December, but the area had record rainfall that year and construction was delayed.

In late fall of 2004 my job ended. Our high-tech company shipped its manufacturing jobs offshore. The need for technical writers diminished and our contract was not renewed. Sixteen of us were let go. Doug was still working and making really good money, so we weren't too shaken by my job loss. The timing was such that I could help Mom and Dad prepare for their crazy but seemingly inevitable move.

In a brief phone conversation with the realtor, I learned that Mom had not been getting the house cleaned so it could be put on the market. Soon after that phone call I entered my parents' house for a two-night stay. It was the first time I had slept there in a very long time.

Mom had always been such a determined and willful person that when she decided to move, none of us thought about dementia. She was just Mom being Mom, a person who wanted her own way and was willing to deceive and manipulate to get it. She had always demanded full control.

Every logical thing I had to say to her, every helpful idea, ran into some new form of resistance. And her realtor was telling her the move was a stroke of brilliance.

"Aren't you excited about your parents' plans?" she asked me.

"No, actually, I'm not. Maybe if they were in their sixties or seventies, but you know how old they are. They can barely survive in this place. A new one will be worse."

From that point forward, the woman had very little to do with me. She and Mom had bonded through the Finnish connection— the husband. Nothing could come between Mom and her real estate agent.

"Everyone I've talked to tells me this is a great plan," Mom told me. Much later, I would find out this was not even close to the truth. "And my real estate lady is such a help."

"Sure," I said. "And you're ignoring the fact that she's after her commission and her husband's fat contract. Of course she's telling you it's a great idea." She dismissed me with a look.

"Stop ruining my happiness! This will be good for us."

Mom's vision was that Chuck would be Dad's companion and she and Margaret would be out on the golf course, having drinks, and shopping while the guys buddied up at home. I hadn't seen their friends for decades, so I had no idea about the state of their own health. All I knew was that they had lived in southern Utah for many years, that their daughters and grandchildren were very close to them, and that soon my ailing parents would be beyond my reach.

Nineteen

opted to sleep in my brother's room. It, too, was a disaster, but at least I could get to the window and open it in hopes of getting a little fresh air.

I started the cleaning project in my old bedroom. The bifold closet doors no longer closed, as the sheer volume of stuff could not be contained. The closet was filled with Mom's golfing outfits, her mink coat, six or seven bathrobes, shoes galore, and a pair of two-drawer filing cabinets.

Mom bustled from room to room, picking up one thing and setting down another. None of it made any sense to me.

"Your dad is such a bastard. I can't get anything done with *Him* around," she intoned, her favorite refrain.

Dad snoozed away in front of the TV set, anything but an obstacle to her or me.

As I had done when I cleaned out the garage, I had to take time to try to absorb all the craziness around me, the vast array of objects, the sheer mass of material heaped everywhere. When I finally dug in, I found some old photos of the house when it was clean.

I held one of them up in my line of site against a sea of debris. "How did things get this way?" I asked myself.

"What the hell?" I muttered aloud, hour after hour, day after day.

Within the first few hours I had already filled both of their trash cans and the recycling bin. Then I unearthed another "treasure": an old glass ashtray. In it were six leaking AA batteries, broken golf tees, a partially chewed piece of candy, paperclips, a matchbook, a drywall screw, and a thumbtack.

I put the ashtray with its contents into a plastic bag and set it out by the trash cans. Kristen and I would make one more run to the hazmat collection site and I'd drop off the batteries then.

All over the floor, under sacks of merchandise from Target, K-Mart, and Mervyn's, I found dozens of old black-and-white photographs. Stuck between some ancient magazines was an eight-by-ten photograph of my dad, Ernest Hemingway, and Harvey Mink. They were holding a dead golden eagle by its wings, Hemingway in the middle, the wings spanning all three men. They smiled at the dead raptor, their shadows cast against the rough exterior of a wooden building I knew must have been in Ketchum. Hemingway had signed the photo: "Best to Jim from Dr. Hemingstein his pal."

It had to be pre–World War II; Harvey was killed on the U.S.S. *Liscomb Bay*, an aircraft carrier that was torpedoed by the Japanese Navy in 1943. I asked Mom about the photo.

"Oh, that old thing. Take it if you'd like. We offered it to the Hemingway Museum in Ketchum and they refused it. They said it was not politically correct with that dead bird in it. And who would believe it's really Hemingway? That photo is signed Hemingstein."

"Mom, Hemingstein is a nickname Hemingway gave himself when he was in high school."

I carefully put the priceless photo in a safe place: when I flew home it was coming with me. It was in remarkably good condition: no fading, stains, or curling edges. I would put it in an antique 1930s frame and archive it with e-glass to protect it. It might not have been politically correct, but it had meaning for my family. My brother Greg's middle name is Harvey in honor of the late Mr. Mink.

I piled up heaps of sheets, bath towels, clothing, and blankets; once I finally figured out what most of Mom's inventory was, it seemed a good idea to stack similar things together and whittle down from there.

Mom had begun freaking out again about all the "valuable" things that were being tossed out.

"Mom, this stuff has no value," I said repeatedly, holding out examples. "Look. This sheet is full of holes. You can't even donate it. That shirt is so stained that no one would even consider buying it secondhand. These shoes are worn out—for God's sake, they're moldy! You have more newspapers and magazines and old *TV Guides* and *Reader's Digests* and *National Geographics* than you could ever read. And the junk mail—what do you need with old, unopened credit card come-ons?"

"Leave those alone. I'm going to read them in Utah when *It* doesn't take up so much of my time."

"What? You think that Dad's going to miraculously change once he moves to the desert? What? Some magical lizard will cross his path and he'll be OK again—just as well as you?"

We hadn't heard a peep out of Dad for several hours. He was snoozing in his chair with the TV tuned to a golf channel.

"Mom, you won't read this stuff. This magazine is dated 1998. And this one is dated 1989. If you can't stand to recycle them, donate them to a library."

On and on I went, justifying my actions, trying to demonstrate that I was making careful and correct decisions. And just as with the garage episode, when I came back to the house after running several errands, most of the things I had moved out of the house had been picked through and moved back inside. When I challenged her, that familiar curt wave flitted in my face.

"Mom. You have thirteen sets of twin bed sheets."

"So?"

"They don't fit your beds."

"Well they're going to Utah."

The next day I found the glass ashtray in her living room, dripping battery acid.

"Mom, that's sulfuric acid leaking out of those batteries. It's dangerous."

"It's mine and I want to keep it. This ashtray is an antique—it's worth something."

We continued talking past one another as I struggled to clean the place and wrest useless and dangerous objects from her grasp.

The house sold before it was listed. The realtor and her broker had a client who wanted to live in that neighborhood for the schools, so a deal was struck and signed. Mom and Dad could have made a lot more money on the house if it had been opened to competitive bidding; houses in the San Jose/Cupertino area were highly desired and it was common practice to solicit bids to escalate the sales price.

But Mom had told the realtor to just find a buyer. "My husband, Jim, does not like strangers in his house, so no multiple listings. We don't want a parade of strangers who will see what we have and then come back and rob us."

Meanwhile, the rain in southern Utah had subsided, and construction resumed on the Coral Canyon house. We learned Mom and Dad could take possession of it in early February. They wouldn't be able to travel there before they moved in, so Chuck offered to do the walk-through and sign off on my parents' behalf.

I returned to the house. The front yard had supposedly been relandscaped, but none of us could tell the difference. The contractor completed the kitchen. Feeling some pressure and knowing that Mom would not and could not prepare for her move, I asked both of my daughters if they could meet me at the house and help.

The garage was a mess again, as were my old bedroom and the sun room. When last I'd left, they'd all been clean. It was as though I had never been there on and off for two years, battling the clutter and filth.

"I thought you were going to stop buying crap you don't need," I said to Mom, feeling defeated and weary. "You've undone everything that I've accomplished. You've even hauled in garbage from the garbage cans."

"Yeah. So?"

"Well, the 'so' part of this is that the moving company will box up everything in this house, including the garbage cans with their contents, and put them in the truck. You'll have to pay moving costs for packing up garbage. Then, in Utah, we will not unpack any of it—I refuse—so you'll be stuck with it in your brand new home. Once again you'll have rodents' nests and earwigs and God knows what else."

She flapped her fingers at me and turned away.

This time I had driven to San Jose in my Explorer SUV because it had a lot of cargo room. Kristen came from Palo Alto and Steph arrived from her home in Bear Valley. I was sure that the three of us with our three vehicles could make a dent in the mountain of possessions my mother had accumulated—again.

We needed a new strategy. We agreed that as soon as we filled a bag or a box we would move it to one of our cars to prevent our very own bag lady from nabbing it back.

Digging deeper into the hall and bedroom closets, we found at least a dozen pairs of shoes that Dad could no longer wear. Because of his congestive heart failure, his feet and ankles had swelled to huge proportions—well beyond cankles, more like thigh-wide thankles. All that fit him anymore were extra-wide sheepskin slippers that would eventually stretch out. Sometimes it looked to me like his skin would split, and he had a perma-cough; he'd hack away every once in a while to clear his chest.

Mom told Dad that I was tossing all of his shoes. He shuffled down the hallway to confront me.

"I'll need those shoes to go with my suits when we move to Utah," he told me. "Your mother and I will be getting dressed up again, so don't throw any of my stuff away. And I need to wear that tie to work tomorrow."

"Don't worry Dad," I said. "I'll make sure that all your things make it to Utah." I'd gotten better at such deceptions with practice.

Mercifully, Mom had to take Dad to the dentist. While they were gone I filled my Explorer with clothing that no longer fit, shoes that could not be worn, and trash that would eventually make it back into the house if Mom found it. Broken clock radios, a chipped plate that said "world's best golfer," and a dusty Hawaiian lei made with fake flowers and plastic shells that had lost their color: all went into a trash bag and into the back of my car.

Dad owned three broken electric shavers. Under a bathroom sink was a toilet plunger that was crumbling to pieces. The shower in the spare bathroom no longer drained. The tub was filled with crumbling plastic bathmats, empty cleanser cans that rattled when you picked them up, and slivers of bar soap glued to the surface.

I filled another bag with dozens of free samples. Whenever Mom saw a basket or a box filled with free goodies in a store, she would take as many as she could carry. Foil and plastic packets filled with shampoo, lotion, face cleansers, eye cream, toothpaste, mouthwash, and sunscreens. Dozens of tiny bottles filled with aftershave, tiny picnic salt-and-pepper packets pocketed from restaurant tables. Deodorant samples. Some of these containers had weakened with age and leaked. I opened the cabinet under the bathroom sink and a pyramid of personal products tumbled onto the floor. Lotions that had turned yellow, products that had separated or dried up in their containers. All of them were unusable, none of them recyclable, all of them destined for the landfill.

We didn't know much about Utah, but we did know that there were no recycling centers where Mom and Dad were moving, only landfills. If we could recycle and donate as much as possible in San Jose, it would minimize what we would have to toss into landfill after the move.

The dust and mold were wreaking havoc on my sinuses and kicking up my asthma. The house was filthy, yet I knew it held treasures.

I carefully set aside things I knew Mom cherished. She had some remarkable family heirlooms. There were dozens and dozens of lace doilies, no longer fashionable but beautifully crocheted by my grandmother and great grandmother. There were books, photographs and frames, art deco candle sticks, Christmas ornaments, and so much more buried under junk mail and garbage. It was a depressing, exhausting chore, but it was also a treasure hunt.

I found two ironstone pitchers that had been on my great grandparents' farm in Minnesota. There were blue glass canning jars galore, some with glass lids. I imagined the green beans, tomatoes, peaches, and pickles that had once been stored in them.

Tucked beside these items was a plastic frog from K-Mart that ribbeted when you touched it. Next to that, a pair of drapes from the long defunct Gemco store: the label said they were made out of fiberglass, and I could see the crumbling fibers through the cloudy plastic wrap. A case of V-8 juice sat on a bedroom closet floor.

Mom and dad returned from the dentist. Mom looked around at the clean spaces.

"Where's all my stuff?"

"I've put things into boxes and carefully labeled them for the movers," A lie, but oh well.

"That's nice, dear," she said.

My daughters were in my brother's old bedroom, which was crammed with the furniture he used when he lived there. Greg had made a lamp that was a replica of Mom's antique spinning wheel. Kristen found an insect cocooned in a double fold of tape, the other end of which was attached to the lamp. No one knew how long it had been there or why it had stayed there when it could have easily been put in a trash can.

Kristen found dozens of old airline booze bottles, those tiny ones that offer one drink, all empty. Next to them she found an empty Ambien container. We looked at each other with raised eyebrows. Kristen did an excellent mimic of Mom when Mom was drunk and offered a short performance until Steph interrupted.

"I won! I won!" she yelled.

Kristen and I, standing knee-deep in old clothes, blankets, books, office supplies, and kitchen gadgets, looked over to see what she had found. We waded through and dodged around the debris covering the floor and stared at what was in Steph's hand.

It was Mom's stool sample dated 1988. Steph had found it in the top drawer of the old desk.

"Cool," was about all Kristen could mutter. "A sixteen-year-old shit sample. That sure beats my taped-up bug." My jaw moved a couple of times, but I couldn't find a word to utter.

My Explorer was jammed with chaos, and I added more chaos to it. The back was filled with ancient junk mail catalogs, old *Reader's Digests*, and *National Enquirers*.

I picked up a copy of an old *TV Guide*. "Hey," I said. "There's over three hundred dollars here."

We were discovering that Mom liked to hide money, so we had to look between each and every page of everything, inside every piece of junk mail, every old Christmas card: everything our hands touched we had to examine for hidden hundred-dollar bills. They were all over the place. We also found a small pile of Series-E bonds that had been issued in our names as well as Mom's.

Nothing could be gathered, briefly sorted, and dispatched. The hidden cash made our jobs that much more tedious. Still, on and on we progressed toward moving time.

Mom opened up a packed box filled with treasures she hadn't seen in years. As she excavated these items, she felt the thrill of discovery. I, on the other hand, wanted to feel the thrill of getting something done, and she was quickly undoing our work.

"Mom," I said. "Let me be perfectly clear. I have a limited amount of time here. You're up against a deadline."

"Well," she huffed. "Are you the new authority in this house?"

"Well, no. But neither are you from the looks of things."

The wave came at my face.

I worried about Dad trying to navigate through all of the debris that was now scattered throughout the house as we worked to first sort it and then dispatch it. He could barely walk, let alone catch himself if he fell. Once down, he was incapable of getting back up unassisted. His old body was too stiff, his muscles too atrophied to grip, his balance too feeble to gain control as he tried to right himself. But almost on an hourly basis, Mom dismissed any concern for Dad's safety.

She was, after all, moving to a brand new house in Utah. She was going to be a member of the golf and country club. She and Margaret were going to have drinks served at their golf carts as they puttered around. Dad was going to be under Chuck's care, and those two ancient pals would sit and drink and talk about the good old days. Mom was convinced that Utah was Utopia. Dad believed it too.

"When we get to Utah I'm going to buy a new car," he told me. "I'm going to get a driver's license and a new golf cart."

Twenty

etween July 2004 and February 2005 I made six trips to my parents' house to try to whittle down the mess before it was all moved to Utah. My family and I foolishly believed that if we gave Mom a boost in the right direction, if we gave her a fresh start by getting her house organized and cleaned, she could take it from there and be able to manage her and Dad's life. When she didn't follow our lead, we believed she was being Mom: a hardheaded, willful woman who could focus only on her own immediate needs. What we believe is often a far cry from reality.

None of us had any legal control over Mom; she was a free person and could do whatever she wanted. All we could do was stand on the sidelines and watch her collide head-on with real life, dragging Dad along with her. We all wanted to escape what we knew was coming: Mom and Dad's failure to live independently.

A month before the moving van was to come to Alderbrook Lane, Doug and I traveled to their house to install a new front door. The real estate agent had insisted that it be updated. Mom asked if we could also wash some windows while we were there. We agreed; since she was blowing through the money she had borrowed through her reverse mortgage, we didn't want her borrowing more money to hire people to do what we could quite easily do. Before we left Oregon I asked Mom if Greg would be there and if we could use his tools for the door project instead of loading up ours and hauling them six hundred and fifty miles.

"No, Greg has some big project he needs to get done at his place," she told me.

On our last day there, as we were wrapping up our tasks and loading our tools back into our truck, Greg drove up and parked at the curb. He looked shocked.

"I didn't know you guys were here. I'm so sorry. I'd have helped if I knew."

"I asked Mom if you'd be around. She said you had to work on your house."

"She never called me. I didn't know."

He apologized again. "I would have been here to help if I'd known. I made squeegees for every size window in my house. I would have brought those and all my tools so you didn't have to lug your stuff down from Oregon."

"Well, our mother said that she called you and that you would be busy. No worries, Greg. We didn't have to work that hard . . . It does seem like the woman is not a reliable source of information these days."

"Was she ever?" he asked.

On our long drive back to Oregon, Doug mentioned that he thought Mom wanted to keep Greg and me apart. "You guys might start comparing notes, and she knows that," he said. "Your mother is still smart enough to know that she's done some weird things and you guys will start talking about them."

Despite her wishes, Mom and Dad's move ended up bringing Greg and me closer. I would find out that this did not please her.

Twenty-one

On a sunny day in early February the moving van pulled up in front of the house. It was 2005; my parents had lived there since 1958. I had no sentimental ties to the place, but it moved me to see all of the old things I had grown up with being hauled into the large truck. I was disappointed to see so many boxes I had labeled "Junk, sort in Utah"—there hadn't been enough time to get to everything. At least the junk was isolated from important and necessary things, although I suspected there might be more hundred dollar bills, credit card statements, or bank account information in the boxes labeled "junk." In the end, the best option we had was to move everything and examine it in Utah . . . whenever.

"Mom," I said, "Have you asked your doctors for referrals to new doctors in Utah?"

I was met with the rude little wave.

"The movers will be here around noon today," I went on, "and you won't find a doctor any time soon when you're in Utah, so you'd better get all the prescription refills you can now. Then you can transfer your prescriptions to a pharmacy near your new place." Mom, taking me by surprise, saw some logic in this suggestion. I called in all of the refills I could find, and the pharmacy told me the order would be ready in a couple of hours. Greg offered to drive Mom to her pharmacy.

One problem was solved, but we still had another one: getting them to Utah. Neither Mom nor Dad could withstand a two-day car trip to the desert Southwest. They couldn't drive there alone. And none of us wanted to weather the five-hundred-mile road trip to southern Utah with them. I imagined with equal horror the joys of being at a motel with Mom and Dad if we drove them, and the traffic accidents Mom could cause if she tried to drive such a long way by herself.

Letting them find their own way to Utah seemed like an irresponsible thing to do from another standpoint. I was just beginning to understand the importance of protecting their wealth, which meant protecting them, too, and keeping them out of the hands of predators who could easily pick them clean. A long drive from San Jose to Utah could expose them to real risk.

At that time Greg and I had yet to discuss Mom and Dad's money situation. They had sold their Alderbrook Lane house for eight hundred and forty thousand dollars. They had an additional seventeen thousand dollars from the sale of their country club membership. They had very little in checking or savings. To survive successfully on their own they needed every cent of their wealth. They had no advance directives, so any major medical event could wipe them out. And Mom was so careless with her junk mail. She wouldn't listen to my warnings about how easy it would be to steal their identity and take every penny they had.

The best idea I could come up with was for my parents to fly from San Jose to Las Vegas and then take the shuttle from the airport to St. George, where Margaret and Chuck could pick them up. We went with that. It would save the Higginses a long trip to Las Vegas and back. I gave Mom the information on how to find the St. George shuttle and advised, "If you get lost at the airport, just ask any of the airport staff to show you where to find the shuttle buses."

After they got to Utah they would stay at Margaret and Chuck's house and wait for us to show up. We planned to arrive in St. George at about the same time as the moving van.

After Greg and Mom returned from the pharmacy, Doug and I took Mom and Dad to the San Jose airport while the movers continued to load the truck. Right after curbside check-in, an airport attendant was waiting with the wheelchair service I had ordered for Dad when I booked their flight. Doug and I walked as far as security and then could go no farther. I watched as the airport attendant pushed Dad's chair to the gate and Mom trailed behind. I knew that if Dad had an accident in his diapers, Mom would not take care of him.

"He can go to the bathroom all by his self," she told me. I knew better. Dad usually peed all over everything, as he couldn't keep his balance during the time it took him to empty his bladder.

"I tried to get him to sit down when he pees," Mom said. "He exploded over that one. Called it sissy. We don't share a bathroom anymore. *Him* can pee where ever *Him* wants to in *Him's* bathroom."

Just before we said good-bye at the airport Mom handed me a fat brown envelope. "Make sure that this gets to Utah," she said.

When the movers were gone we cleaned every room. After packing up their bathroom items, I knew how bad those bathrooms looked. I had briefly met the buyers of Mom and Dad's house. They seemed to be such nice people. They had a little girl who would move into my old bedroom. Maybe it was because of her that I volunteered to clean the bathrooms.

I had to remove the toilet seats to scrub off the shit sprayed all over the seats, lids, and hinges. About every ten minutes I changed my Nitrile gloves. I wore a mask and threw out all of the towels I used. There was no way that I was going to toss that filth into the washing machine, which was staying with the house.

I really wished that Mom was cleaning these toilets instead, so she could get a reality check. She was obsessed with her vision of Utah and how perfect her life would be there. Anything related to San Jose, Dad's failing health, her failing health, poopy toilets, dead bugs in pill vials, or loads of junk mail barely got an eye twitch from her. It was Utah or bust for Mom.

Twenty-two

The day after my parents flew to Vegas, Doug and our dog Maizie piled into our car while Kristen and I got into my parents' Ford Taurus. Mom had donated her spare car to the Salvation Army, but she insisted on keeping her Taurus. Doug thoughtfully brought along a set of walkie-talkies so we could stay connected when our cell phones failed.

It took us all day and late into the night to get to the Utah house. Mom had given us a key, and we had brought sleeping bags, pillows, and air mattresses from home. It was too late to stop by Margaret and Chuck's to let the oldsters know we had arrived. When we pulled into a small store at a gas station, we realized that we were in the middle of nowhere and there was nothing at the new house for us to eat or drink. We loaded up on bottled water, juices, energy bars, paper towels, and toilet paper.

"Hey, Mom," said Kristen, unpacking the toilet paper, "I know where there are two hundred rolls of this stuff smelling delightfully of rodent."

It was pitch dark when we arrived at the Coral Canyon development, so we saw nothing of the Utah desert. We had some road food, and that was our midnight dinner. I called the Higgins house the next morning and asked Margaret and Chuck to let Mom and Dad stay at their house while the moving van was unloaded and we put things away.

"Dad falls a lot, and there will be way too many tripping hazards for him until we can clear up all this chaos," I said.

Every hour we worked on my parents' move, I grew increasingly resentful toward my mother. She had no business pulling a stunt like this. Dad was ninety and she was eighty-six, for crying out loud.

"Yeah," Greg had said before we left San Jose, commiserating about the folly of it all. "I tried to have a conversation with her before things went too far. But she insisted that it was a good thing for them. Seriously, neither logic nor reason apply here."

Once in a while I took a stretch break, sore from bending over dozens of boxes. I walked around the new house, nibbled an energy bar and drank orange juice. The place was lovely: high ceilings, good layout, and a half-acre backyard I went out to investigate. Part of it was fenced; the rest was a natural desert hillside, so different from what I was used to in Oregon.

Along the side of the backyard, the view went on forever to the western edge of Zion National Park. Although I'm not a fan of lizard land, I could appreciate the drama of the southern Utah desert, which was beginning to be drenched with rain. I went back into the house to unpack some more boxes.

"Maybe it's time to have the oldsters come over," I said. "Mom might want to have some say as to how her house gets put together."

"Let them sit and have their coffee," Kristen said. "We'll see them in a couple of hours."

The moving crew was organized motion and by one o'clock the truck was empty. There was still no sign of Mom or Dad. I called them at Margaret and Chuck's house and asked them to come over and bring the checkbook. The moving crew needed to be paid before they left.

Mom used her credit card and shelled out close to seven thousand dollars for the move. While business was being conducted in the kitchen, Dad, Margaret, and Chuck roamed around, looking at how things were coming along.

As soon as the movers left, I suggested that the oldsters return to Margaret and Chuck's house. It was only two o'clock but Mom had obviously been drinking already. The floors were littered with boxes, slippery bubble wrap, and newspapers. All the more to worry about for unsteady Dad.

They took my advice and after they were gone, we got in our car and drove around looking for food. There were twenty-six hundred acres of nothing but houses, a golf course, and a club house. If you needed anything else, it was either east to the small town of Hurricane or west to the larger town of St. George. There was nothing of the essentials nearby for Mom and Dad: no grocery stores, no pharmacies, no medical centers—and no family once we were gone.

It took us almost two hours to drive to St. George and back to buy a couple of bags of groceries.

Doug, Kristen, and I worked well into the night putting Mom and Dad's beds together, unloading clothes into the huge walk-in closet, and sliding furniture around to best fit their new abode. Doug hooked up the TV set, and Kris and I prepared a simple pasta dinner. We showered and watched TV for a few minutes before we all gave up and went to bed.

On our fourth day we proclaimed the house habitable and gave Mom and Dad a tour of their new home. Their beds were made and bathroom and kitchen items had been put away, so those rooms were fully functional. The living room was in order, complete with art on the walls. We made room in the garage for Mom's car. The other half of the garage was filled with boxes.

"Mom, all you have to do is tackle one box per day and you'll be done. Most of this is just stuff we didn't get to in San Jose. Everything else is put away inside."

Mom kept asking the same questions over and over again. "Where is everything? Where's all my stuff?"

"Mom," I responded again and again, "just open a closet or a cabinet and you'll find all your stuff. Everything is in a logical place. Your important papers are in the same filing drawers as they were in San Jose. Nothing is missing. It's all here. Including this." I handed her the fat brown envelope she had pressed into my hand back in California.

The night before our drive to Utah, while we were eating Thai take-out in Kristen's living room, I had opened the envelope. It contained more than seven thousand dollars in cash.

I assured Mom once again that all she had to do was look for her things and she would find them. "By exploring you'll get familiar with your new place. It's all here."

(Well, it was all there except for a couple of tons of garbage and useless items we had sent to landfill, recycled, or donated.)

Mom kept asking about how to pay her mortgage. While still in San Jose, Greg had patiently repeated, "Mom, there is no mortgage. You paid cash for your new place. The rest of the money from your old house went to your bank. Just go to a bank branch in Utah to access your money and get the address changed on your accounts."

The new house was smaller than the old one, but it had a huge covered patio where we put all of their outdoor furniture. Since none of us had seen the new place or even a floor plan before the move, it was hard to determine what to bring and what to leave behind. It turned out that despite the generous patio size, only a fraction of Mom's collection of ragtag outdoor furniture should have been moved.

Doug, Kristen, and I took one last tour to make sure things were as OK as we could make them. As we took full stock of the new place, we shook our heads at the choices Mom had made. The guest bathroom had a full bathtub. There was no way Dad could lift his legs to get in or out safely. The master bathroom had a huge jetted bathtub, even more of a problem for Dad. But his dementia was getting pretty bad at this point, so he just went along with whatever Mom suggested. They both seemed to think their new house was perfect for them.

Dad believed Mom when she told him Utah would be their fountain of youth. He told us he was going to drive a car again and golf. His bockety old legs could hardly support him, and his round feet caused him to pitch and roll when he tried to walk. He agreed to use a cane, but he wanted no part of his walker, so we put it in a closet where he couldn't trip over it. He had just started to use the walker in San Jose; now that he was in Utah, he was supposed to be young again.

"Walkers are for old people."

"Dad, you *are* old."

He just grinned.

It was good to see Margaret and Chuck again. Margaret was just as beautiful as ever and Chuck's wit still keenly sharp. Before we left, the three of us were checking out the laundry room together when Chuck said, "Your mother is not the Lila I remember."

Margaret concurred by saying, "She just needs be happy."

It seemed Margaret and Chuck had observed my parents' rancor and bitterness during their almost week-long stay. The four of them had been close in their younger years but they hadn't seen each other in a long time.

Both couples were too old to travel much, and Margaret and Chuck were surrounded by family who lived nearby. Aside from living near their old friends, Mom and Dad were now isolated in the vast Utah desert. We left them looking out their dining room window at the pouring rain as we waved good-bye from our moving car. Later, we would regret not flipping coins and making bets as to how long Mom and Dad would last there.

Twenty-three

We had hoped to do a bit of sightseeing before Kristen flew back to Palo Alto and we headed home, but by then we were exhausted and, unbelievably, Utah was even soggier that winter than Oregon was. It was time to head home. First stop—put Kristen on a plane in Las Vegas.

After we dropped her off, Doug and I headed west to Santa Ana to see his dad, Hal. Being that far south, we saw a good opportunity for a visit, and I was desperate for Hal's calm and organized home and his sweet personality.

I called my brother from Hal's home. "Really, the Utah place is a nightmare. It's more than two thousand acres of housing, plus a country club. There are no stores there at all—no grocery stores, no department stores, and no medical clinics or dental offices. Not only that . . . Mom made some really bad choices when she picked the options for this house."

I told him I was troubled by thoughts of Mom getting lost while driving, and that I could picture Dad acting out in frustration when he found out that the house wouldn't work for him, especially when he couldn't find his familiar things. I described all the falling hazards I'd seen, especially the bathing situation. "I worry about Dad's hygiene, and she won't bathe him or hire anyone to help him," I said.

In my mind's eye I saw terrifying images of Mom having a high-speed car accident. Despite living for decades in the Bay Area, the woman had never driven on a freeway in her life; she had always depended on side roads and her knowledge of nearby terrain. She was a stranger in Utah, and she would have to buy groceries on Highway 15, where the speed limit was seventy-five. It wasn't a great stretch to imagine Mom trying to pull onto that road in the old Taurus with Dad yelling, "Just goose it, Lila!"

Worse yet, Dad could insist on getting behind the wheel just to show her how it's done and get them both killed.

"I'm just not sure how these oldsters are gonna get along, Greg."

We found out sooner than we expected.

Twenty-four

The first phone call came about a month after they moved into their new house. Mom complained that there was no one to talk to. She got lost all the time. Dad was always in his chair doing nothing and she couldn't get a damned thing done because he took up so much of her time. It was a familiar litany.

"And he's starting to smell," she said. There was a new refrain.

"I thought you and Margaret were going to spend your days golfing and drinking and shopping."

"Margaret has arthritis in her hips. I wish I had known that. And they're always busy with their family."

"Well, Mom, you moved away from your family. And you were with Margaret for a week before you even bought the house. You knew that walking was hard for her. Chuck has to help her in and out of their car. You saw that when you were with them. Why is this a surprise?"

As usual, our conversation ended with her discounting me and my obvious frustration. I could hardly suppress my deep desire to say, "Told ya so!"

By April, Mom was anxiety ridden, and she was bitter about having to spend Easter all alone. Margaret and Chuck had their big family. Back in California, Greg and Kristen had usually joined Mom and Dad at the country club for Easter Sunday brunch. Now there was no family around and nowhere for her to go. They were as isolated as I had tried to tell her they would be.

I called Chuck a couple of days later and learned that Mom regularly went out for groceries and came back confused, having been lost for several hours and returning with no food.

"Karen, I got to tell you. We're old too and we can't keep an eye on your folks. I've got Margaret to take care of. She has heart problems and had to have a toe amputated and her hips are bad.

109

I'm losing my eyesight to macular degeneration. The only time I can drive is in bright daylight. I can't be your mother's chauffeur."

A couple of weeks later both Chuck and Margaret called. Chuck went first. "Your mother was gone for over six hours. Your dad got lost trying to walk to our house to look for her. It's over a hundred and ten degrees out."

Margaret added, "He had no hat on and looked like he had been lost for hours himself. His zipper was down and his shirt was filthy."

"He was almost panicky when he found our front door," Chuck continued. "Looks like this move was a bad idea."

Margaret and Chuck lived only seven doors down from Mom and Dad, but Dad got turned around quite easily and all the houses looked alike. Margaret and Chuck had given him a stiff drink, and Chuck had walked him back home, arriving just about the same time Mom finally pulled into the driveway. She had gotten lost—again—on Highway 15.

"There's no place to turn around for miles and miles. I had to drive over thirty-five miles before I found a place to turn around. Those big trucks scared the hell out of me," she told me when I called to ask her what had happened.

Decision time came on Mother's Day. I called Mom with the usual greetings. She sounded awful.

"I fell last night. Hit my head."

"Call a taxi and get some medical attention."

She refused that advice. No surprises there.

"*Him* had gone to bed. I was drinking my wine and stood up to get a refill. Then I woke up on the floor with my head bleeding."

"How long were you on the floor?"

"It was dark when I fell and it was light out when I woke up."

"Mom, once again, I strongly advise you to get medical help. I can call a cab from here and have them pick you up. There are medical facilities in St. George."

She refused again, saying that she'd be okay, and then fell silent.

Then the Mom-bomb detonated.

"We realize that this is not working out for us. We're going to come and live with you."

No, no, no, no, hell no, fuck no, no way! This idea scared me more than any of Mom's other harebrained schemes ever had.

"No," I said firmly. "That is not an option. We live in a wilderness area. There's nothing out here for you. Dad would fall all the time. We have no pavement, only gravel and dirt and pastures, nothing smooth. Doug and I are in town for twelve to fourteen hours a day. Our closest neighbor is a half mile away."

I shut up then and tried to gather something closely related to a complete thought.

"Look, Mom, if you want to move again, we can help you, but this time it has to be to assisted living. You can move back to California or up here near us, but you cannot live with us. Our place is small." *And Doug would divorce me.*

"Well fine, we'll live with Greg then."

"Mom, that won't work either. There are stairs—you know Dad can't climb stairs. There are no convenient medical offices or grocery stores. You are not living with Greg. It's assisted living or you have to stay in Utah. Take your pick." My heart was pounding in fear at the very thought of them under my roof, or my brother's.

"You can choose an assisted living place in Utah if you want to stay there, but again, there will be no one to take care of you or Dad. So it's probably either back to the San Jose area or up here— but not at our house." The more times I said that, the better I felt.

She decided Oregon sounded good.

Doug might divorce me yet.

"OK Mom, now listen. You'll be moving on *our* schedule this time. Doug is swamped at work, so the sooner we can get this done, the better."

Good job asserting your authority, Karen. I knew time held no meaning for my parents.

We ended our conversation with my pledge to help them find assisted living. I knew there were a couple of new facilities in our area.

I couldn't wait to tell Doug this latest news. He'd be thrilled.

Twenty-five

One of the new facilities was just outside Corvallis with lovely views of the countryside. It was surrounded by pastures filled with sheep and dotted with the llamas that watched over them, and it was close to the foothills of the Coast Range where we lived.

Immediately after hanging up the phone with my mother, I called Chuck and told him that Mom and Dad would be leaving Utah as soon as we could make plans. I asked him if he knew of a good real estate agent to get their Utah house listed.

The first weekend in June I flew to Vegas, took the shuttle to St. George, and then took a taxi to the house. The real estate agent had told me they wouldn't show the house until I arrived. She had observed that Dad's dementia was getting worse and strangers startled him. She thought it would be best if I was there before the parade of lookers came along.

After nine hours of traveling, I was beat, but I knew that most of my exhaustion was from the anticipation of what I would find.

Mom had lost a lot of weight; she couldn't have weighed more than ninety pounds. She had developed a strange skin problem I can only describe as whole-body dandruff. "I'm shedding like crazy," she had told me on the phone. "I can't stop scratching. It must be the dry climate here, or maybe I'm low on iron." The true cause was likely malnutrition. I later learned that her daily meal was cream cheese smeared on a slice of bologna and that was it until cocktail hour, which never started later than five.

I had tried to brace myself for what was coming. From the front door past Mom's skinny frame I could see the chaos, the havoc that was her new house. I hadn't realized it was possible, but it was worse than anything I'd seen in San Jose.

The realtor and the first potential buyers would be there the next morning at 11:00. I couldn't drink the cheap wine Mom and Dad drank so I dug out a bottle of brandy I had unpacked back in February and poured a small amount. I wanted a shower, as I reeked from the smoky haze inside the Vegas airport, but I also wanted to spiff up the house at least a little before I showered and retired for the night.

I chatted with Mom and Dad as I straightened up newspapers and wiped off soiled kitchen counters. Mom had brought boxes into the house, half unpacked them, and left them and their contents where they lay when she became bored or distracted.

"See," she said, gesturing to them, "I can't get anything done with *It* constantly lazing about." I could scarcely believe I was back in the vortex of that broken record.

The carpet in front of their twin recliner chairs was horribly soiled, the terminus of a trail of spillage from the kitchen—where, on the tile floor, was a stain. "What's that?" I asked Mom.

"That's where I fell and cut open my head." She leaned toward me to display a half-inch scar above her eyebrow. I looked back at the floor. The tiles were twelve inches square, and blood stained the grout of at least three of them.

"I think I had another TIA that night. It felt like the last two or three, the one just before my fender bender at the gas station in Saratoga. Things just go blank."

The bathroom countertops were cluttered with old toothpaste and dozens of product samples. There was hair everywhere. From the looks of them, neither of the toilets had been cleaned since I'd left. The sinks were full of tiny food particles and scum.

There was no time to cope with all the filth before the first potential buyers arrived. I did as much as I could in the kitchen: I wanted this house to sell. As soon as a deal was signed, I could go back home.

Mom and Dad retired around ten that night. I noticed that their piles of pills were gone. I knew she still poured their medications into little heaps, paying no attention to dosing instructions. The medicine would be swallowed in the evening with a big slug of cheap wine.

"Mom, that's a lot of wine to be drinking with all those pills," I had said when I had first witnessed their routine last winter. "Dad takes phenobarbital as an anti-seizure medicine. That's a bad idea with wine, and then an Ambien on top of that."

"So what. We only hurt ourselves." I, and my worry, apparently didn't exist.

By midnight I was finally in the shower, homesick as hell and a bit buzzed from the long day and the brandy. I couldn't wait to get home where life was sane and clean and organized and safe.

The next morning I started snooping through all the paperwork I found lying around. There was a Visa statement with a balance of more than eleven thousand dollars. The payment was overdue, so the company had been socking them with astronomical interest rates. I found an overdue Sears bill with the same steep late charges. There were numerous notices from the California DMV letting her know that the Taurus's registration had expired.

"Mom, did you know that your tags have expired on the Taurus? Why didn't you get your car registered here?"

"It's too hard to find things here. I tried to change my driver's license. They wanted me to take a written test."

"And?"

"My California license is still good, so why bother?"

I tried to tell her that with expired tags and an out-of-state driver's license, which she should have replaced within her first thirty days in Utah, her insurance was most likely kaput too.

Then I found a paper trail showing that she had renewed her California policy and then applied for a Utah policy as well. There was a refund check for almost seven thousand dollars accompanied by a letter from the moving company saying she had paid them twice. She had not deposited the refund and it was almost a month old.

Chuck and Margaret came by and offered to visit while the potential buyers came through. I thought it was a good idea. Chuck seemed to calm Dad and Margaret was the sweetest woman I knew.

"I was just asking Mom about her Utah driver's license," I said when they arrived.

"Yeah, the old gal flunked her test three times," Chuck told me. "The last time she walked into the testing room with the driver's manual. Thought she'd help herself to an open-book test and she still missed passing by three points."

Mom overheard and tried to defend herself. "The rules are different here."

Chuck patted her shoulder. "Well, it's all turning out all right. You'll be in assisted living where you won't need a car." To my surprise, Mom smiled with what looked like relief.

Later Chuck explained that he had driven Mom to the DMV in St. George each time.

"You've been good to them, Chuck, and we appreciate it," I said. I decided it was time to tell him the full story. "We all tried to talk them out of moving here. They could have just come for a visit, but Mom wouldn't hear of it. She said she had to live here and that you were going to take care of Dad so she and Margaret could drink, shop, and play golf."

Chuck laughed at the thought of him being Dad's day care. "There ain't no room for your dad on my dance card. I am filled up with Margaret's needs as well as my own," he said. "Hell, we need our kids and grandkids around to help *us* out. No way can we fit your parents into that situation."

"I know. Mom just wouldn't listen to our advice to get an in-home caregiver for Dad or move to assisted living in San Jose. Now we have to move them again."

"Yeah, you kids have had to do a lot for them. And you've done the best you could. Anyone can see how hard you've worked."

Eleven o'clock arrived all too soon. The agent came a few minutes early and then another agent arrived with a middle-aged couple. They were moving to St. George from Colorado. They had sold their house, so there were no contingency problems. They had the cash, the credit, and the desire to move into my parents' neighborhood.

They told us they wanted to look around the neighborhood some more and left. Five more couples came through. At six o'clock that evening the first couple returned. They were truly lovely people and they made a great offer. I urged Mom and Dad to accept it on the spot.

Before the buyers left, the gentleman asked to have a word with me. We went out into the backyard, pretending to be looking at the landscape and trying to find out where the timer for the sprinklers was located.

"I am not sure how a four-month-old house could get so filthy so fast, but our deal is off if this place is not spotless when we take possession."

He cleared his throat and went on: "I will not have my wife gagging and throwing up trying to clean that toilet in the master bathroom."

"I assure you that this place will be clean. This house reflects two old people who can no longer live on their own. It will be clean," I told him. "I'm sorry it's not spotless today. I just got here late last night."

Mr. Buyer asked me not to bother with the soiled carpets— they would rip out the carpeting and put in ceramic tile. But everything else had to be pristine.

The realtors informed me they would give Mom and Dad a copy of the signed agreement the next day. There would be a thirty-day escrow and Mom and Dad could sign their part of the paperwork using a notary in Oregon. I was hugely relieved.

That night, I showered and packed, more than ready to go home. Before my taxi came to pick me up, Mom and I walked around her house. I put sticky notes on all the things she wanted to move to Oregon and a different-colored sticky note on the things that were to be donated to charity.

We came across her TV trays, still in the hall closet where we had left them. "I don't want those anymore," Mom said. "I should have left them in San Jose."

This surprised me. Those TV trays had been their kitchen table. Every night they sat in their recliners, drank wine, watched TV, and put their plates filled with overcooked, processed food on those rickety metal trays.

"OK, if you're sure. Once things are left behind, they'll stay here."

"Yes, I'm sure. Get rid of them."

I was overjoyed to see Doug waiting for me at the airport in

Portland as I came out of the baggage claim area. We talked and planned all the way home, trying to come up with a scheme that would work. The logistics were overwhelming.

First, we needed to find a facility that had a full bedroom separate from the living area. So many assisted living places offered studio-type apartments and Mom would have none of that.

Then, since they would be flying in, we had to solve the riddle of how Mom and Dad could live in the new place with only the contents of a couple of suitcases until everything else arrived. There was packing and cleaning the Utah house, finding medical and dental support in Oregon, and planning and carrying out another big move. Doug had to schedule time off, burning up his paid vacation time—once again—on my parents. For my part, I had heard a couple of rumors that I might be offered my old job back, and even though there were no dates attached to the rumor, I had to be available for that. I had to move quickly.

And how would Mom and Dad navigate the flight north? By the looks of things, I would have to accompany them.

Twenty-six

Several weeks later I flew into Vegas again, deplaned, and entered the airport's smoke-filled terminal. I was beyond annoyed that my life was being disrupted in so many uncomfortable ways: once again my mother was back in my life, making her problems my problems.

I spent the next two days filling as many suitcases as I could with my parents' things. I had a small carry-on bag. We were allotted two suitcases each so I could fill six in all. I packed clothing, medications and important paperwork—just enough to last them for up to two weeks. I washed everything so they would have plenty of clean underwear, pajamas, and comfy clothing.

The assisted living arrangements had been made. The place they were moving to had a spacious one-bedroom apartment available, but it was unfurnished, there was only a fridge, so they offered Mom and Dad the temporary use of a guest apartment. It was fully furnished and stocked.

They could have all their meals in the plush dining room or in their own room, as they chose. Their kitchen lacked a dishwasher or a stove. The latter was a relief since Mom was a fire hazard, as she often left hot pads and kitchen towels on the stove burners and walked off to do something else.

The day before we left St. George for our flight to Portland, I drove Mom to the nearest Walmart, where she had transferred their prescriptions. As I had in San Jose, I urged her to get refills just in case.

There was a long line at the pharmacy counter. Near us was a crying toddler sitting in a grocery cart. The child's father was trying to calm him. I watched in horror as Mom walked up to them and, with her face mere inches away from the child's face, yelled a fake crying sound—"Wah! Wah! Wah! See? I can cry louder than you."

"Mom!" I grabbed her arm and steered her away from the shocked father and sobbing child. "You may *never* approach someone else's kid for any reason! Never!"

She just looked at me laughed. She found herself hilarious.

We finally got the drugs and went out into the baking sun to the car.

"Oh, I forgot to get some more diapers for your dad," Mom announced.

"I'll go get them," I said, thinking she probably just wanted to shop some more,or maybe find another small child to scare. "You stay here with the windows down. It'll take me just a minute."

When I came back to the car Mom's head was tilted against her shoulder. Her mouth was open, her eyes closed. She was pale and her breathing was shallow. I worried that the heat might have done her in, or perhaps she'd had a stroke or a heart attack. I was just about to reach over and pick up her wrist to feel her pulse when her eyes opened.

"So what's going on?" she asked, looking around as if she'd never seen that place before. It took her a while to get her bearings but then she seemed fine and I relaxed.

On the day we left Utah for Oregon, Dad was confused and disoriented. He repeatedly asked where we were going and for how long.

"Well, forever, Dad," I said. "You and Mom cannot move again once you're in Oregon. Well, you *could* move, but I wouldn't help you."

"And thank gawd for that," Mom said. "I'm ready to get settled."

As much as I wanted to chastise her for putting this mess in motion in the first place, I kept quiet.

"Time to go," I said. "Our flight leaves at eleven."

At seven I was behind the wheel of Mom's Taurus. I turned to my parents. "Say good-bye, house."

Mom and Dad waved good-bye to their four-month-old home, then to Margaret and Chuck as we passed by their place on our way out to Highway 15.

I floored it all the way to Vegas, surprised that Mom's Taurus could do eighty. At curbside I handed over the luggage. I reached in to help Dad out of the car and into his wheelchair.

"I have to go to the bathroom," he said. Then again, "I have to go to the bathroom."

"OK, Dad. We'll get you inside to the men's room."

Then a foul smell filled the car and I knew Dad's bladder was releasing—it was too late to make it to the bathroom. The odor was horrible, as it always was, whether the result of his failing kidneys, dehydration, or the cocktail of meds he took every day I didn't know.

After I checked them in electronically, an attendant came to push Dad in his wheelchair to security.

"Dad needs a bathroom," I told the attendant.

"I don't do bathrooms," she said. Well, that was clear.

"Mom, can you help Dad?"

She walked away ahead of me.

I hurried after her. "Mom, Dad needs a clean diaper."

She threw up her hands. "Too bad. He can just tough it out."

I had left the car at the curb while helping my parents into the airport. "I have to go park the car," I told the attendant. "I'll meet you at the gate." I handed her their boarding passes. In the parking structure I sat in the car for a few minutes, collecting myself.

I *should* be a daughter who could change her dad's diapers without batting an eyelash, or gagging over a trash can. But no matter how hard I tried to even approach that task, I choked. Stage fright, revulsion, fear of seeing my father's private parts, odor—I couldn't sort through the possible reasons. But there it was: I was unable to help out Dad with his bathroom issues. Still, for me, personal hygiene was a must, and imagining Dad with soiled pants made me feel negligent. But such an invasion of his privacy was a much larger issue, for both me and him. This situation screamed of his need for a caregiver.

More than ever, I needed Mom and Dad to be cared for. I needed someone else in the picture who could control the diaper rashes, my mother's irrationality, the insane amount of filth that they lived in, and most of all, Mom's mindboggling spending habits. I hoped that an assisted living situation—closely supervised by me—would ensure that Mom and Dad could have a good life now.

I desperately wanted my sane life back, with my husband, my children, my dog, and my tree farm. I wanted nothing more than to watch the wild turkeys dart around in search of food and the deer nibble at fallen apples in my orchard. I craved the serenade of the coyotes' howl-fest in the dark hours of early morning. Instead I had bodily fluids, cigarette smoke, and the chaos of a busy airport.

My house was always spotlessly clean and my husband and I were responsible, hard-working people who always got things done and kept in mind the goal of a better future. My mother, at this point in her life, was a train wreck. Despite the discomfort of our present circumstances, I held a fervent hope. Maybe I could help her get back on track. Maybe I could be that influential person who helped her see that there was still a good future for her and for Dad too. It would take patience, consistent reasoning, and a logical approach to life, but it just might work.

I had parked the car on the top floor of the multi-story parking garage. I made a mental note of the location. The car still reeked of Dad's urine and it wasn't lost on me that I had parked in the P aisle. I put an envelope in the trunk for Kristen. It contained enough money for her to pay for the airport's long-term parking fees and gas for the drive to Mom and Dad's house. After we got Mom and Dad settled in Corvallis, Doug and I planned to drive back to Utah to clean out the house and pack up. Kristen had offered to join us to help, so before I left home I had mailed her a spare car key. I had also made plans to sell the car to Mom's banker, who was buying it for his sister, a college student. He would come and get it a few days after Kristen's arrival.

Upon re-entering the airport, my hopes for the future forgotten for now, I felt overwhelmed. Here I was in lizard land longing for the Oregon rain. I couldn't believe how homesick I was.

Mom and Dad and the airport attendant were quietly waiting at the gate. Our plane would be leaving in less than a half an hour. I had booked three first-class tickets on this flight, probably their last plane trip, and there was no way Dad could navigate the plane's long, narrow aisle with his walker without lots of legroom.

We got settled in, and the flight attendant offered them champagne and snacks. Mom and Dad felt pampered. Soon after take-off, Mom fell asleep. I moved over to sit next to Dad. He had a window seat and his mind came back to life. He could name all the mountain peaks from Utah to Oregon.

"There's Lassen and Shasta, and there's Wizard Island in Crater Lake, and there's Three Sisters." And on he went to Mount Hood and what was left of Mt. St. Helens. "There's the Columbia River."

Just before landing Mom woke up, seeming disoriented. She chugged the rest of her champagne.

An airport attendant wheeled Dad from the plane to the baggage claim area, where I called Doug on my cell phone. He had been waiting in our car just outside the terminal.

"Could you line the backseat with plastic bags and cover them up with that beach towel? Dad's had an accident and I don't want our leather seats getting ruined. I'm not sure if his diaper is leaking, but the smell is awful."

As I was pulling the luggage off the carousel, Doug appeared. I was overjoyed to see him. Dad said to Doug, "This place sure has a lot of trees." Mom slept some more on the two-hour drive from Portland to Corvallis, but Dad stayed awake, curious about the terrain in his new home state. "Is that the Willamette River?" he asked.

"No Dad, that's the Tualatin River, but we'll see the Willamette as soon as we get to Corvallis. The next river we'll cross is the Santiam," I said. "Doug and I live near Mary's River."

As soon as we got to the assisted living facility I asked the receptionist if Mom and Dad could have some refreshments in the dining room. "I'm sure they're hungry and thirsty from our long trip," I said.

While they were enjoying their late afternoon snack, Doug and I unpacked their suitcases and put things away in their temporary apartment. They were given a tour of the facility, and then we gave them a tour of their place. We walked with them to the dining room where the staff was waiting to greet them. After Mom and Dad were settled in for their evening meal, Doug and I left and went home, showered, and summoned the energy to fix ourselves something to eat.

The next day I took my parents to their first doctor's appointments. The director of the facility had booked these appointments as soon as I paid for the deposit on their apartment.

"All new residents must have a doctor's checkup before they can move in," she had said. "We have to know of any special diets, their medications, and any other information that will help us care for them. Many of our residents have some dementia problems and they are not able to tell us about their special needs, so we insist that they get checked out before living here."

"Can't their families help out with that information?" I said.

"Sometimes they can, but you'd be surprised to learn that many people in assisted living care facilities, as well as in memory care facilities, get dumped there by their families. We had a lady who was brought here by her family and they didn't come back until three years later when she died and they had to empty out her apartment. Some families are no help at all."

In the reception area there was a poster on the wall letting people know that if they needed the help of an ombudsman, they should call the person listed.

"What does an ombudsman do?" I asked.

"He ensures that no one here is abused. He's here for the protection of our residents," the director answered. "If anyone in the family is abusing one of our residents or stealing their money, he is the one to call for help. And if anybody on staff is abusive, he'll step in and get things straightened out."

It was good to know there was someone designated to defend these oldsters. I took the time to tell the director about my parents: their abusive marriage, Mom's harebrained schemes, their fragile health issues and that Mom could be difficult. There was no compelling need to tell her any of this at that point, but my intuitive voices were telling me I should at least give her a heads-up.

Their new primary care physician examined them and checked out their list of medications. Mom had been taking an over-the-counter iron supplement.

"Why are you taking extra iron supplements? Have you had a recent blood test?" he asked Mom.

"I have anemia," she told him. "I just know I have it and it's making my skin itch and peel. I've been taking a lot of iron pills, but it doesn't seem to get any better." The doctor raised his eye-brows and ordered blood and urine tests.

Dad's weight was close to two hundred and thirty pounds. He was five feet six inches, only three inches taller than me; he had once been five feet nine. Mom weighed eighty-nine pounds and was four feet ten, down from five feet two. I hoped the good nutrition at the assisted living facility would help them both.

After two hours at the doctor's office and lab, I stopped at Rite Aid to get their new prescriptions filled and Mom went in with me. She lugged two gallon jugs of Carlo Rossi into the cart. She also picked up two bags of Dove chocolate candies, two bottles of V8 juice, some mixed nuts, and licorice. Then she wanted to stop at the grocery store and load up.

"Mom, you never need to buy groceries again. You and Dad get all of your meals at assisted living. And you don't have a full kitchen, so you can't cook. You can only heat up your leftovers in your microwave or store them in your fridge."

She looked confused, but I left it at that. I was tired. She would catch on to her new routine. I dropped them off. It was late afternoon when I started my long drive home.

Spacing out at a red light, I entered a one-way street headed the wrong way. I immediately pulled over and at my first opportunity turned around. I had lived in Corvallis for almost thirty years and knew it well; I had never gotten confused before. I was so tired I was becoming worried about my own safety.

The next morning when I got up and looked in the mirror, I saw Sasquatch looking back at me: mangy hair, puffy face, dull eyes. Despite my exhaustion, I had had a bout of insomnia, only managing to get to sleep at about four-thirty. I was starting my day by running late. I didn't bother brushing my teeth or washing my face, and all I could do with my hair was rip a couple of bobby pins through it to keep it out of my eyes. I had just enough energy to get dressed and leave the house.

Stepping into someone else's life was brutal. I seemed to be permanently occupied with my parents' lives and sadly ignoring mine. The resentment I felt toward Mom was huge. She was such a stupid woman, ignoring all sensibilities. Her actions paved a rough road for all the rest of us. I was trying to be an honorable daughter and protect them from their own foolishness. But Mom and Dad had always been foolish, squandering their happiness to keep their decades' old battles alive and well, never considering that my brother and I had lives. There was no reason to expect anything but difficulty.

After a lot of prodding from me, Mom finally saw the value of having important legal documents on file in her new town. My attorney provided me with them, and they were notarized at the bank when I took Mom and Dad to transfer their accounts and change their address.

"Advance directives are important," Mom told the notary. "No one will put me on life support. I'd rather die."

I dropped the signed papers, including durable power of attorney documents, at the attorney's office; they had appointed me as their representative. They also signed a will with Greg and me as their beneficiaries. Since they no longer owned real estate, a simple will was all they needed, but Mom insisted on having a trust and appointed me as trustee.

"Mom," I said, "you have no assets to put in a trust. You own no home, you have no car, you have no huge investment assets. All of your money is either in savings or checking accounts and the one annuity you bought in Utah. The rest, by the way, should be invested in something."

On my drive home I thought about why I had left California—to distance myself from my parents. I loved Oregon and the miles that separated me from them. Now they were here, easy access, close by, making me available to their demands. But what other choice was there?

Greg had once provided their long-term care; he was always available. Now it seemed that they were my responsibility. Fair enough. It was time for Greg to get his life back. My parents were invading mine, and I was filled with regret that I had ever gotten involved, but again, I could see no other options.

My hope was that they would settle into assisted living and enjoy all of the resources the Corvallis community offered its senior citizens. Assisted living was a whole paradigm shift for my parents and I truly wished it to be a good experience for them.

Selfishly, I also hoped they would become so occupied with their new life that I would become a mere shadow hanging on the sidelines.

Their facility offered many activities and was a beautiful place, with outdoor areas and covered balconies, a library, a huge dining room, several alcove rooms, a nursing office, and dozens of private apartments. It reminded me of an upscale hotel. I was hoping that Mom would find friends to socialize with. There was also a small golf course, similar to one in California she had enjoyed, and a senior ladies' group.

But constant nagging thoughts plagued my sleep. I knew my mother. I knew that when she wanted something she would find a way of getting it. No matter how much I tried to reassure myself and tried to believe that having my parents close by in protective assisted living would be good for them—and me—there was still plenty to watch out for. As much as I tried to comfort myself with these thoughts, my tingly neck hairs refused to relax. My pesky intuitive voice would not be silent.

Twenty-seven

Two days after Mom and Dad's medical checkup, Doug and I were in our car on our way to Utah once more to move their things to Oregon. We were doing it ourselves instead of hiring movers to save them a couple of thousand dollars. We drove east through Bend and spent our first night in Mountain Home, Idaho, then headed south.

When we arrived at Coral Canyon, the house was just the way I had left it before rushing Mom and Dad to the Vegas airport.

"What the hell happened here?" Doug asked. "It was clean when we moved them here. Hell, it's a brand new house."

When we had moved them to Utah in February, we organized everything for them. After we left, Mom wrestled the boxes we stacked in the garage into the house. She opened most of them and scattered their contents everywhere, making the new place look very much like the trash heap that had been their San Jose house. And even though Mom frequently got lost in the St. George area, she somehow managed to buy plenty of junk that now blanketed the junk from San Jose.

The first thing I did after unpacking our car was to clean the house as much as I could for our own comfort. At least Mom's bathroom was fairly clean. Just to ensure our hygiene, though, I scrubbed the tub, sink, toilet, and floor. I wondered if Mom's skin problems, her shedding that Kristen would soon call "Granny flakes," could be due to her lack of hygiene. She seemed cleaner than Dad, but I had no idea how often she showered.

I filled a trash bag with product samples she had stockpiled. I threw away her old dirty hairbrushes, toothbrushes, depleted toothpaste tubes, and any other opened personal products I could find. I gave away a lot more: her apartment at assisted living was fairly spacious, but there was no extra room to store everything she had hoarded. If it was an unopened product, I put it in a box that would eventually go to a local charity or food bank.

My next project was to clean the master bathroom, intent on keeping my promise to the new owners that this place would be spotless.

The huge oval bathtub was clean but I scrubbed it anyway. It dawned on me that Dad might not have had a shower since he left San Jose, as he couldn't step over the high-rimmed tubs in this house. Mom didn't care enough about Dad's hygiene to do anything but carp about it. Their new home in Oregon had a huge walk-in shower, big enough to accommodate a wheelchair and with no raised lip to trip over, just a solid nonskid ceramic tile floor.

Once the master bathroom tub and shower were clean, I moved on to the toilet and sinks. I don't gag, but I gagged. I'm not squeamish, but I became so: the buyer had been right to protect his wife from this experience. The toilet was covered in feces. Lifting the seat revealed a much worse mess than I had found in the San Jose house. There were feces splattered on the walls and on the floor. I put on a protective mask and Nitrile gloves. I stacked rags and cleaning supplies on the floor. I unscrewed the toilet seat and took it out into the backyard.

Using a long-handled scrub brush that I dipped in a bucket of hot water, bleach, and soap, I scrubbed off every molecule of human waste. I rinsed it off with the garden hose and then let it sit in the hot Utah sun to dry. Doug came out and sat down next to me.

"Déjà vu," I said.

"Déjà poo," he shot back.

Without the seat attached, the toilet was a bit easier to clean, but with each stroke of the sponge along the tile floor where the toilet sat, a small backflow of brownish fluid appeared. I was not about to remove the toilet and wipe under it, so I kept rinsing and wiping and rinsing and wiping until only clear water appeared, telling me that finally Dad's brown mess was taken care of. I screwed the toilet seat back on.

There were double sinks in the master bathroom and Dad had used only one of them. There was a veneer of spit, food chunks, dried-on whiskers, hair, toothpaste globs, and soap scum covering the sides and drain hole of the sink. The faucet was splattered, making it look like some kind of corrosive chemical had eroded it. The mirror was mottled with more splatters.

Once again I put on my protective mask and gloves and used full-strength bleach to vanquish the horrifying mess that glazed that sink. Rubbing my gloved fingers over the surface of the sink, I could feel that the chunks were not coming off, so I plugged the sink and filled it with hot water and let it soak. Meanwhile, I scrubbed the tile floor on my hands and knees. After several hours of soaking, the sink finally came clean.

By then I was wiped out and nauseated. I was hungry but only wanted bland things to nibble on and gallons of water to drink. I found Doug again in the garage. He was sweating profusely.

Our plan was to clean the garage, sort out what would go to Oregon, and set aside what would stay in Utah. It made sense to put all of the Utah donations in the garage where they would be easy for the collection crew to get at. Then we would put the move-to-Oregon stuff in the empty garage and finish the scrubbing job; an empty house is very easy to clean.

Sorting and cleaning the garage was crucial to our schedule. When Mom and Dad had arrived in this house, the garage was orderly, with every box labeled, stacked, and sorted according to its contents. In the large floor-to-ceiling storage cabinets in the garage we had put like items together: big batteries with small batteries, all the light bulbs in one spot, tools all together, and luggage items with other luggage items. Nothing was as we left it. The few tools we had taken to Utah were missing. Where I had put the light bulbs I now found several months' supply of Campbell's soups.

In the laundry room I found twenty-eight bottles of salad dressing. The laundry products sat in a heap by the back door.

"Mom and Dad can't even eat salads anymore, their teeth are so bad," I remarked to Doug as I put the dressing bottles in a food bank box.

In the silence of my parents' house, Doug and I mumbled "What the hell?" from time to time as we came across one nonsensical scene after another. In the bedroom we had set up as an office for them, I had organized stacks of important paperwork, putting various types of paperweight on top: a ceramic figurine, a small rock from the backyard, or a hardbound book. On the wall above these stacks I had taped a sign: DO NOT TOUCH!

"Mom," I had implored, "I've spent hours sorting everything here, so do not touch it. When Doug and I get back here to pack up your things I'll deal with this paperwork."

She had nodded her head in agreement. But now, standing in front of my once carefully sorted categories, I could see that nothing was left of my system. "Oh bloody fucking hell," I muttered.

We talked ourselves into quitting at around ten o'clock that night. We had pasta with pesto sauce, bread, and steamed broccoli and then went to bed on our air mattress and sleeping bags.

We got up at 5:30 the next morning, wanting to finish up the garage before the Utah sun rose and the temperature began its climb to a predicted 112 degrees. We created three distinct spots in the garage as we had done in San Jose: donations, trash, and what would be moved. We battled both anger and disappointment that Mom had created such chaos where there had once been order.

By early afternoon, Kristen arrived in Mom's Taurus. We took a lunch break and sat in the dining area, unable to move, unable to find the energy for it. All I wanted was to sit in an air-conditioned movie theater and sip Coke and eat popcorn. All Kristen could do was mutter, "What the hell?"

"I don't know what to do next," I said.

We decided to empty out all of the closets—just dump things on the floor and sort, sort, sort. Our choices were fairly easy; we knew that with their failing health, their activities would be limited.

There was no way that Dad could ever golf again, so all of his golf gear—cleated shoes, jackets, and golf shorts—went into a charity box. Mom's one-piece jumpsuits followed; she had lost so much weight that she was about three sizes too small to wear much of her clothing. We also sorted to accommodate Oregon's climate, choosing the warmer items like sweaters and warm pants.

While Kristen and I went through the closets, Doug dismantled the twin beds and leaned them up against the wall. I had stripped them, and the bedding was in the washer. Next we sorted the contents of the dressers, keeping only what would fit in Mom and Dad's new space and suited Oregon weather. The filled boxes and bags meant for donation went out to the garage.

Every once in a while we took breaks and went outside, but the huge backyard was unbearably hot. When we had been there in February, the creek adjacent the property had been gushing with abnormally heavy rain. Now it was dry. Earlier in June when I had been there to set up the sale of their house, I had stood in their backyard and watched the ash fall; summer had brought severe wildfires. My eyes had watered from the smoke, but their backyard had been the only place I could get cell phone reception. Now in early July the heat was such that we could only stay outside for a few minutes at a time.

Mom had managed to find her way to the grocery section of the Walmart in St. George, and all she did was buy, buy, buy. In addition to the twenty-eight bottles of salad dressing there was an astounding amount of food: peanut butter, jams, jellies, processed foods, and chips and cookies and crackers.

"Mom and Dad get all of their meals cooked for them now, so I see no reason to move any food to Oregon," I said. Doug and Kristen agreed. We filled more than twenty U-Haul boxes with food for the local food bank. At long last, the laundry room and pantry were empty of food items. We packed up all the dishes and some kitchen items.

"Mom and Dad can't cook anymore," I said as I stowed things away. "All they can use is their microwave, sink, and fridge. I'm thinking Mom doesn't need pots or cooking utensils."

"Good thing, too, since Gramma's always putting flammable things on her stove," Kristen reminded me.

We filled boxes of kitchen items for donation. I kept some food storage items, all of the dishes she had collected or inherited, and some of their glassware. Sorting by what they could and couldn't use in assisted living made our decisions straightforward. Soon our project was running smoothly and we no longer needed to consult with each other about what to leave and what to take.

By the time evening came around, we had our dinner in front of the TV and relaxed for a few moments. We had to cover Mom's chair with beach towels in order to sit on it; her "Granny flakes" covered it. All of us were too tired by this time to tackle anything heavy, so I pulled out some boxes that had been moved from San

Jose to Utah, labeled "Junk, sort in Utah." I set a box in front of each of us.

We saved any paperwork that had to with banking or real estate and any receipts for tax purposes. The rest—junk mail, magazines, and catalogs—we pitched into garbage bags since there were no recycling centers in the St. George area.

Rummaging through a box filled with old receipts, junk mail, used napkins, and grocery lists, I hit pay dirt. "Wow. Hundred dollar bills!" I said, waving them in the air.

These wouldn't be the last we would find. During the course of our five-day stay we found close to thirteen thousand dollars in cash, mostly in hundred dollar bills. That was the good news. The bad news was that we couldn't throw away anything from boxes labeled "junk," and we couldn't assume that anything in those boxes didn't have cash tucked away in it. We had to sort through every magazine page, every envelope, every piece of junk mail, looking for Mom's money. We felt like we'd never finish the job, since not a single box from San Jose had been dealt with, only opened, rifled through, and then abandoned.

I asked Kristen what her travel expenses were and reimbursed her with part of the cash. "Mom said for us to tell her what she owed us for helping out," I told her. "So here's yours." The rest I would put in her bank account as soon as we returned to Oregon.

We saw quite a bit of Margaret and Chuck while we packed up and cleaned out my parents' house. Chuck gave me the number for a Mormon charity and I called and set up a time for them to pick up the things we were leaving behind. We wanted to be on the road back home by the time Kristen's plane left that coming Sunday.

The charity truck was supposed to be there on Thursday afternoon—it arrived late, and there was only room in it for one dresser. I called the office and asked them to send out another truck the next day. They were booked solid and they didn't pick up on Saturdays or Sundays.

"You have no idea how much stuff there is," I told the office worker on the phone. I was nearly in tears. "If we don't have someone come to pick it up we'll have to haul all of it to the landfill." Finally she agreed to send out another truck on Saturday morning with a crew.

I thanked her profusely. "You won't regret this. There are so many useful items here."

Hugely relieved and realizing how quickly our departure date was approaching, we worked late into the night. The office, master bathroom and bedroom were done; the kitchen and laundry room were done. The closets were all empty. Once the charity crew had emptied the garage, we could fill it with things to load on the truck Doug and I were renting.

On Friday morning Doug and Kristen went to pick up the truck and a trailer for our car. I stayed at the house, as the banker who had bought Mom's car was coming by to pick it up.

Mom had paid cash, more than two hundred and fifty thousand dollars, for their Utah house. With the rest of the equity from the San Jose house, that left more than five hundred thousand dollars to invest. She had bought an annuity from this young banker and put the rest into a money market fund. Other than the loose cash that we were still finding everywhere—the most recent discoveries under a lamp and inside books—all of Mom and Dad's assets were accounted for.

I feared that Mom didn't fully realize how terrifically expensive her moves had been. With moving expenses, real estate fees, and everything else, I calculated that they had lost over a hundred thousand dollars. Still, they had plenty, and the money from the sale of this house would transfer to their new bank branch.

The charity crew arrived early Saturday morning. Kristen used a clipboard to write down each item as it went on the truck and I took photos for tax purposes. The three men had the seventeen-foot truck loaded in less than two hours. I photographed the crew, the truck and once they were gone, the empty garage. Then we started moving furniture out to the garage, staging it for loading into the rental truck the next morning. We knew that not everything would fit into my parents' new apartment, so before leaving Corvallis I had made arrangements to put the excess— things such as antiques and family heirlooms—in storage.

Saturday morning Chuck came over to help us load the truck. Though he was in his late eighties, he stayed through to the end, helping us like a man in his forties. By ten o'clock, we were feeling the worsening Utah heat, but we were done. Doug hooked up the trailer so we could tow our car behind the rented truck. At least we could keep each other company on the long drive back to Oregon.

The three of us spent the rest of the day vacuuming empty rooms and making sure that every space was vacant and very clean. The next morning we had a light breakfast. I flagged down the mail carrier and gave him a change-of-address card. I had asked Mom if I could forward her mail to my address. I was determined to make sure that all of her bills were being paid, and I could start putting a permanent stop to all that junk mail. "That would be nice," she had said. "Less for me to worry about."

We dropped Kristen off at the Vegas shuttle stop in St. George. Hugs, kisses, thank you, and see-you-soons. Then we drove through the Great Basin toward home. When we hit the concrete pavement on Highway 80, our U-Haul truck bumped and jiggled with such force we had to pull over and retighten the tie-downs to make sure our car on the tow trailer was secure. All along the road side we saw huge locusts, shocking in size. They must have been a plague to the farmers of the area.

We spent the night in Wells, Nevada, in a filthy room in a cheap motel that reeked of urine. Neither of us dared to go barefoot. I even wore my flip-flops in the shower the next morning and insisted that our dog Maizie sleep on the bed with us. I imagined us hauling home bed bugs, Legionnaire's Disease, flesh-eating bacteria, or all three. The squalor seemed a fitting end to the Mom-and-Dad-move-to-Utah chapter of our lives.

Twenty-eight

We spent the next night in Bend, Oregon. It was only about three hours from home, but we were so road weary, having been bounced around on concrete pavement for many hundreds of miles, that we pulled over. We left early the next morning, and by ten o'clock we were pulling into the parking lot of Mom and Dad's assisted living facility.

The staff of the assisted living facility met us to help unload the furniture. While they and Doug moved my parents' things into their new apartment, I packed up their belongings from the guest apartment and moved them too. Then Doug turned in the truck. He came back to pick me up in our car, newly liberated from its trailer.

We were very happy to be home. I had planned on seeing my parents about twice a week. As it turned out, my visits were more frequent than that, as their health was so poor. They had been so incapable of caring for themselves that they were malnourished. Mom, in particular, was skin and bones. "She looks like she just escaped from Auschwitz," I told my brother.

Almost every day there was a trip to a doctor or dentist. Mom called me all the time. "Could you come by tomorrow? I need something from the grocery store." I took her and Dad to the local DMV to get Oregon ID cards. I had Dad's doctor fill out an application for a handicap parking permit. There were banking errands to run and paperwork to look after. And this was just the beginning.

When Mom and Dad closed escrow at their bank branch in Corvallis on their Utah house, I went with them. As soon as the money was in Mom's bank account she bought two more annuities. Before leaving Utah I had asked the banker at the bank's branch in Hurricane to forward Mom's annuity information to the Corvallis branch.

I assumed that it had been done.

Twenty-nine

After less than a month of being in assisted living in Corvallis, Mom announced, "We want to move."

I couldn't believe what I was hearing. "Where?" I asked.

"We want to live in Idaho."

"Who is *we*?" I asked, knowing that Dad was not capable of thinking up a plan like this. "What about Dad?"

"What about him?" she retorted.

"Well, he's very old and he's not healthy. Moving would be bad for him." *Bad for me too.*

Dad turned ninety-one a month before they left Utah. His dementia was bad most days. He often forgot my name and couldn't remember what he had for breakfast. Symptoms of congestive heart failure were obvious; his blood thinners made his skin a blotchy purple, as though he'd been severely beaten. Added to that, he had several lesions on his face, most likely more skin cancer.

Doug and I were exhausted. Work had been piling up at our forty-five-acre tree farm. We had taken no vacation time that year since we had used so much of Doug's paid time off tending to Mom and Dad's two huge moves. I was still in a layoff situation until further notice and I should have been using my free time to work on our needs, our place, our farm—but I had no free time. Mom and Dad's demands were huge. If I were called back to work, my life would be screwed. Mom alone was more than a full-time job.

If I ignored her demands when she called me at home, she complained to the staff and they called me. "Your mother is out of panty liners. Your dad is out of adult diapers. They need toothpaste. Your mother complains that her dentures don't fit. Your mother won't let us in to clean their apartment. Your mother's claiming we're stealing her laundry. Your mother yelled at a food server this morning. She's refusing to take her medications."

It was hard to keep up with it all. In trying to restore their health, they had many doctor and dentist appointments. To be an effective caregiver I had taken to keeping a calendar and a day planner dedicated solely to them. I had been a top producer in the technical writing field, able to keep everything organized using a few sticky notes and my ability to remember numerous details. Organization was something I had always been very good at. But now, with my parents in town, I woke up each morning in a fog of mystery. I simply wasn't able to keep my usual mental calendar of upcoming events. And I hated to rely on organizers. It made my life seem scripted and that felt stifling.

Through that first summer and fall, Mom continued to complain. Almost every time I saw her she said she was moving: Idaho, back to California, Florida, Minnesota, Australia, New Zealand. Each time it was different.

Eventually Thanksgiving rolled around. I truly did not want Mom and Dad visiting us. Our place is very rugged and remote, with two miles of gravel road just to get to the driveway and another half mile of gravel to the house. There are no smooth surfaces to walk on around the house, and there are steps on all sides. Indoors are either thick carpets or slippery bare floors, both tripping hazards for Dad. We were thirty-five miles out of town, and there were no emergency services to help him if he were injured. And not least of all, I didn't want them in my refuge; our home was a place I could be free from Mom's constant bitching and Dad's wet diapers.

Shortly after they moved to Oregon, my mother had told me she wanted to come to our place.

"Mom," I told her, "it's at least a half an hour to your apartment, then another half hour plus back to my place. And to bring you back here and for me to drive home again, that's over another hour. So I'll have a two-hour road trip. Between all of your doctor and dentist appointments and your constant shopping, when do you think I'll have the time to bring you out to my place? Plus, the trip would be hard on Dad."

"Your father doesn't need to be with us," she snapped.

"Mom, I am not going to play that sort of game with you and Dad. All you'll do is lord it over him that you got to see our place and he didn't. For now, there's no time to chauffeur you all the way out to our farm anyway. When you stop asking me to take you shopping every day then maybe we'll plan something."

I could have let Mom ride the bus that the facility offered its residents when she wanted to shop, but I knew her spending habits were out of hand. At least when I was with her, I could control how much she bought and how much she spent. This plan served its purpose, but it robbed me of hours, days, and weeks.

Just before Thanksgiving I told Mom that I had made reservations at a swanky restaurant in town for our holiday meal. Greg was taking the train from San Jose to join us. She said the arrangement was fine with her and it would be fun to go out and have a nice meal together. So it was all set. We'd pick up Mom and Dad and have a relaxing dinner and they could take home all the leftovers and savor them later.

"I will enjoy eating out and ordering a real cocktail," she told me. "The food at this place isn't always very good."

She had been complaining about the food all along, but every time I was with her in the dining room, her plate was clean. Her fridge was filled with leftovers from other meals. So she ate heartily, but this didn't stop her from complaining whenever she could. She gained weight, almost fourteen pounds. Her skin problem cleared up: no more granny flakes. Her hygiene and Dad's seemed to have improved, probably because the shower was more accessible. Dad had a shower chair so he could sit while he washed.

Over the holiday, Greg spent time with Mom and Dad and toured their assisted living place. "It's really nice," he told me. "A lot more plush than I thought it would be."

Greg had visited Dad whenever he was in a nursing home recovering from a stroke or a once-in-a-while case of pneumonia. "Those places weren't very nice, so I had no idea what to expect," he said. "I almost didn't want to come here, knowing how awful some of these places can be." I was quite relieved to hear that. We agreed about their care, and I wanted him to approve of what I had done so far.

When Mom had first told me that she wanted to live in Oregon, I had called Greg and asked him what he thought: should we move our parents back to California or up here? Since assisted living was more affordable in Oregon, we based our decision on that. Both states had about the same in quality and services, but here their money would go further. Greg was happy that quality hadn't been sacrificed to save some bucks. "At least this place doesn't reek of bathroom odors as soon as you come in the door," he commented.

We spent Christmas morning at Mom and Dad's and then went home for a quiet evening. While we were at the facility, Mom told me, "They're stealing my things." By then I knew everyone on staff and they were great. I went to the office and asked them about what Mom had said—she had mentioned a couple of cheap plastic laundry baskets in particular as missing. They were quickly located, downstairs in the laundry room. I brought them to Mom and asked her if they were hers. She had been marking her name on everything, and sure enough, her name was on the baskets.

"No," she said. "Those are not mine. Mine were stolen." There was no point in arguing. I returned the baskets to the laundry room.

"My TV trays are gone too."

"Mom, you left those in Utah. You told me to get rid of them."

"No I didn't. I need those trays. I use them all the time. They were just here."

When Mom and Dad were due for their six-month checkups, I tried to tell the doctor about my parents', especially Mom's, disturbing behavior.

She overheard me and she was furious.

"Look what she's saying about us," she hissed to Dad. She stood up and moved to slap me, I stepped back a few inches and she missed. The doctor shot me a look of surprise. I asked to speak with him out in the hall.

"Can I talk to you about Mom's behavior without her being present?"

"No, I'm afraid not. Whenever I discuss your mother, she has to be present. Even though you have power of attorney, the HIPAA laws—that's the Health Insurance Portability and Accountability Act—protect her privacy. You can put your concerns in a letter and I'll read that, but I can't discuss her with you in her absence."

So I made a bulleted list of what Mom was doing. I started with how she was medicating herself and Dad, paying no attention to dosing instructions and taking them all at once with very tall glasses of wine.

"Doctors say that wine is good for you," she said the first time I commented on this.

"But Mom," I objected, "you and Dad drink sixteen-ounce glasses and then refill them. Doctors do not say that a quart of wine, or more, each night is good."

In response to my letter, her doctor ordered that all their medications were to be dispensed by a medical aide. This service would cost them four hundred dollars a month each, but since they were in a licensed facility and it was recommended by their doctor, the expense would be tax deductible.

"I hate this," Mom said. "They stand there and wait for you to take the pills."

"Well then, just take them and the med aide will leave."

"I feel like a two-year-old."

"You're acting like a two-year old. I'm sorry you feel that way, but since you pay no attention to what the labels say, your doctor feels that you can't handle this responsibility."

"I feel like a child."

"Mom, get over it. Just take your pills and the med aide will leave you alone. They don't like it any more than you do."

On the list I also included information about the filth she and Dad had lived in for the past several years, that she left kitchen towels on the stove burners, and that she had an eleven-thousand-dollar balance on a credit card that had been past due for two months while she had hundreds of thousands of dollars in assets. She was paranoid, afraid to meet new friends, and accused every-one of stealing from her when she misplaced things. Mom con-tinually accused Doug and me of stealing her TV trays, the ones she insisted on leaving in Utah, even though we had photographs of them being loaded onto the charity truck and they were on the itemized list of donations we prepared for her tax return. Finally,

I wrote that she was extremely mean to Dad and he was too frail to fight back.

The tables had turned in my parents' marriage. Dad had been the offender in their early years. Now Mom was the stronger one, and for her it was payback time. She made the advances, the first strikes. All Dad could do was hunker down and wait for her rampages to end.

Her complaints about him were endless. When she was offended, she literally turned away from the scene. She started sitting sideways, facing away from him at their dining table. That was typical Mom behavior.

"Just look at *Him*," she would hiss. "He's disgusting." Pointing with her thumb, she'd say, "Can *It* get anymore pathetic?"

During one visit, the complaint ran like this: "He pooped in his pants again. I am so sick of this. Then he called me a bitch when I was cleaning it up. I told him that he had to stop doing this, making me wait on him like this. I'm not his maid or his servant. I get a life too."

Not for the first time, I told her to call the staff to help her with Dad when something like that happened. "Mom, it's what they do. It's called *assisted* living."

"Oh no," she said. "He'd be embarrassed if anyone tried to help him."

On a hot August day I drove to the facility. Just to the west are steep hills, but most of the grounds east of the buildings are flat and smooth, flowing out to the valley floor. As I approached the parking lot I saw Mom storm-trooping up the sidewalk on the steepest part of the hill. It had to be ninety-five degrees outside. Behind her, Dad struggled to keep up, shuffle-clomping with his walker. He was sweating profusely and not wearing a hat, and Mom kept turning around to yell at him.

I signed in at the front desk and went to the nurse's office.

"Yes, your mother is behaving rather badly," a nurse told me. "We don't have a lot of control over her. Your dad does whatever she tells him to."

I went outside and asked Dad to come in. "There's some cold lemonade waiting for you," I called out. He seemed relieved, but his trip down the hill scared me more than the trip up. I worried that his forward motion would send him sprawling downhill, tumbling over the walker he had finally consented to use. Bravely I walked in front of him, intent on breaking his fall if needed. I walked slowly so he didn't have to struggle.

Mom walk-ran in front of us. "He's getting fat. All he does is eat, so he needs his exercise," she carped all the way back to their apartment.

Dad sat for a while and cooled down, sipping his lemonade. I sat on a footstool across from him waiting for him to have a heart attack. I was again convinced that one of my parents could kill the other. Dad looked at me for a while.

"You are beautiful," he said to me. A compliment from Dad was weird, a complete surprise. Not knowing what to say, I just murmured, "Thanks, Dad." Then I left for home.

Thirty

During their first seven months in assisted living Mom continued to demand that we move them again: to Idaho, California, Florida, Minnesota, New Zealand, and Australia. She insisted that her present arrangement had never been her idea.

"No," I said firmly one day, having finally had it with her stuck record about moving. "No. Not only are we never moving you again, but no and hell no and even fuck no!" I moved close to her.

"We will never help you move again," I said, more softly this time. "Do you understand that?"

After that things changed between us. She became very secretive, but by then I was close to several of the staff members, and I heard a lot about my parents. It was good to have informative resources.

In January of 2006 Mom was referred by her primary doctor to a neurologist. During an annual physical she started spewing to her doctor how unhappy she was. Most of what she said was irrational, such as her demands to move again to places where she and Dad could never survive on their own, like New Zealand. Her doctor noticed that her demands were illogical and even unsafe.

A few weeks later he did a complete neurological workup, an MRI, and a mini–mental state exam (MMSE), which is used to assess many cognitive functions. Objects are held up for identification. Memory recall is tested, both old and new memories. Copying a graphic and drawing an abstract object are required. Small physical tasks are required as well, such as standing on one foot or touching fingers to the nose with the eyes closed.

The MMSE test is scored numerically from one to thirty, with thirty being the healthiest. Mom scored a twenty-nine, which was excellent. But her MRI showed a different story; there were huge black spots in my mother's brain. Where grey matter should have been there was nothing, and that nothingness was filled with spinal fluid. Her behavior also told a different story from the MMSE.

Six months later in a repeat MMSE evaluation, Mom scored a seventeen, which put her in mid-dementia range.

"Your mother has Alzheimer's," her neurologist told me. This was truly bad news, and at the same time, I felt vindicated. I had known something was terribly wrong and suspected Alzheimer's. For some time now she had moved beyond her characteristically prickly personality into a new realm that felt much more out of control.

Mom was given an Alzheimer's drug and an anti-psychotic drug to help alleviate her paranoia. I had great hope for these, but unfortunately, they take a long time to be effective and must be given in ever-increasing doses.

In April of 2006 Mom told me again that she hated assisted living and once again demanded to move.

"Go ahead," I told her, tired of the battle. "But we won't help you."

She went on to tell me about a woman whose husband could no longer stay in assisted living. Apparently he had health issues that required more skill. "This woman has moved to a lovely apartment right in town where she's close to shopping and theaters and dining."

"Mom," I tried to explain. "This is Corvallis, a very small town. Close to theaters? There's a community theater downtown that used to be a movie house. The other movie house closed years ago. There's a run-down four-plex north of town. Fine dining is available in a few places, but mostly there's just fast food or pizza. This is a university town, after all. And look, there isn't really a 'right in town.' You have to have a car to get to all these places — they're scattered north and south, not all in one central spot."

I had been ferrying Mom around the town for ten months by that time. She didn't remember any of it.

Thirty-one

My Uncle George lives in Arizona. He was married to Delores, one of my mother's sisters, who died in 1984 of lung cancer. After her death George left their home state of Minnesota and moved to the sunshine and warmth of Surprise, where he met his second wife, Renee. She died of ovarian cancer in 2006. After her death I flew to Arizona to see George for a couple of days. He is such a delightful man, and the last of my uncles. I consider George to be a close friend as well as a dear relative.

While I was staying with George, my husband called me.

"I just got a call from your mom's bank," Doug said. "Your mother has been there, and she wants to know how to revoke your power of attorney. She also wants to have her mailing address changed to her own address, and she wants a copy of all of her bank records."

I felt nauseated. The hairs on my neck stood up, and my intuitive voices screamed. I had known she was up to something. She had been too quiet and too secretive lately. I flew home a couple of days later and called an attorney.

I told him all about my mother's harebrained schemes to move, the filth she created, the danger she put my father and herself in, the mismanagement of their medications, the financial mess she made and how I had cleaned it up. And I told him she had recently been diagnosed with Alzheimer's. We discussed the possibility of petitioning the court for guardianship and conservatorship of both of my parents. He gave me a list of things he needed, such as an accounting of their assets. "Conservatorship is solely about the money," he told me. "The court will want you to prove that their wealth will be protected."

The lawyer continued to ask me about my parents and their

ability to take care of themselves. I told him as much as I could and included Mom's accident in Utah and the tremendous amount of dental care they both needed.

"Mom fell in Utah. The bloodstains were quite large from a cut on her head," I said. "When we talked on the phone I insisted that she get medical care but she refused. I saw the bloodstains when I went to Utah to set up their move to Oregon." I went on to fill him in on all their health issues.

"When Mom still lived in San Jose her dentist pulled out all of her upper teeth and put in an upper plate that never quite fit. Dad had dental problems too, but not as serious as Mom's."

Our dentist in Oregon had to pull most of Mom's remaining teeth. All she had left now were two lower front teeth where her lower partial clipped on. "Your mother has osteoporosis," the dentist told me. "The bone loss caused her to lose her teeth. And it's the bone shrinkage that makes that upper plate wobble. She has a few sores in her mouth from the plate rubbing along her gum line. We can fix it, but it will be expensive and it will take time, as that upper plate has to be resized."

It took several months for all of her dental work to be completed. Her upper plate was in fact salvageable, but we had to wait for the lower area to heal after the extractions so she could be fitted with a new partial.

Dad had to have oral surgery to remove two impacted wisdom teeth.

"Your father gets to have milkshakes for dinner tonight, but he cannot use a straw. Sucking on a straw could cause him to bleed, so have him use a spoon," the oral surgeon said.

On our way back to assisted living, I asked Mom and Dad what flavor of milkshakes they wanted. Mom, who was sitting on the back seat, started making strange gurgling noises. When I looked back at her, I saw that her eyes were wide open. I immediately pulled into a fast food parking lot, worried about how quickly I could pull out my cell phone and dial 911.

"Mom! Are you all right?"

Dad, who could no longer turn around due to his heft and his stiff body, asked, "What's going on?"

Mom gurgled a bit longer, her lower jaw moving up and

down. I reached for my purse to get my cell out. I flipped open the lid and typed in 9. I was about to type 1 when she spoke.

"I'll have chocolate," she said.

"What?" I asked. Now she looked completely normal, sounded normal.

"I'll have chocolate, two of them. One for now and one for later."

Mom had that history of TIAs, and they affected her speech. The first one she had, or that we knew about, happened at a gas station where she fender-bent another car. Insurance cards were exchanged, damage repaired, and everyone moved on. She told me that she never remembered her TIAs, but her friend Bev told her that she stopped speaking when she had one.

By the time we got back to Mom and Dad's apartment, she was sipping her chocolate shake like nothing had happened. I gave Dad's pain relievers to the medical staff and asked them to make sure he didn't start bleeding. He would have a recheck in a couple of days and his stitches would dissolve.

On Mom's and Dad's last day at the dentist, she was handed a bill for almost eight thousand dollars. She gave me her checkbook and asked me to write the check; she would sign it. I noticed that her once lovely handwriting was shaky and almost illegible.

"Geez, Mom," I said when we were back in my car. "I thought you said you and Dad were getting dental care in San Jose. I know you didn't have a dentist in Utah, but you were only there for a few months."

"Our dentists in San Jose said we were fine," she told me. I was only beginning to find out how many professionals blew off the elderly, skimming over their needs and billing them for big bucks. Our own dentist and his staff were the best, so I knew that Mom and Dad would finally be taken care of.

I also noticed that the elderly don't always accurately describe their pain. Nor are they necessarily able to tell you where it is. One nurse told me that Dad fell a lot because his kidneys were starting to fail as a result of diabetes. But he never seemed to exhibit any signs of pain after he fell. He told me that he didn't feel well, but he was very vague: "I'm just fine, dear."

After telling the lawyer the details about their state of health

I told him about Mom's behavior in public places. It seemed to be getting worse every time she and I ventured out.

At one time there was a store in Corvallis specializing in Scandinavian items. Mom liked that they sold items made in Finland. Since it stocked original art, it was an expensive place, so I only took her there a few times. The last time was for their going-out-of-business sale. Mom rushed around the store manically, pulling off the shelves everything she could find that said "Made in Finland." She found plates and table linens and wood carvings and coffee mugs and Finnish flags—none of which she would be able to use at the facility.

"Mom, what are you doing? You have no place to put all of this stuff."

"You just don't want me to have things!" she yelled, standing in the middle of the store and glaring at me.

All around the store, shoppers looked up and watched as she stood in a defensive crouch, holding her selections to her chest.

I tried to ignore the others in the store. "Just a few more minutes, Mom," I said in what I hoped was a soothing tone. "I have a meeting to go to, so I have to leave." That last part was a lie, but how else could I get her out of the store without throwing a tantrum? She continued to pile things up at the counter. Her purchases totaled two hundred and ninety-four dollars. I had to tell her three more times that I had to leave before we finally exited the store.

To get back to the car, we had to cross a busy street. While we were waiting for the light to turn green, she stepped off the curb. I put out a protective arm.

"What would happen if I did this?" she asked, stepping another foot forward.

"Well, you'd get run over, that's what," I said.

A young couple standing near us gave me a shocked look, horrified that they might have to witness an old lady being run over on the street while we all looked on.

❖

I related this tale and to the lawyer, saying, "It hadn't dawned on me before that Mom might be planning suicide. She did hoard medications, but then she hoarded almost anything she could find. When she wanted to leave Utah she had asked me about Oregon's assisted suicide laws. I had told her that they wouldn't apply to her; they only applied to those who had a terminal disease that would cause death within six months. Alzheimer's is a fatal disease, but it can take its toll over decades, not months. She started asking me about assisted suicide again, and after a while I just changed the subject.

"She's terrified of Alzheimer's and the many other dementia-related diseases," I continued. "She sneers at the people at her facility who display signs of mental deficiencies."

"Ain't that pathetic?" she would comment. Meanwhile, I was noticing her paranoia becoming worse almost every day, so her renewed interest in assisted suicide alerted me to one more thing I had to watch out for.

I thought about what would have happened if Mom had stepped in front of a car. What could I ever tell that driver? Oh, she's old. No worries, she was dying anyway. Or what if a driver had swerved and hit someone else? Or what if the driver was hurt? Now I had a whole new crop of things to worry about.

"I believe it's crucial that someone have custody of these two," I concluded. "I seem to be the most logical person to take on that responsibility."

The attorney and I ended our meeting. I was tasked with providing him with a list of my parents' assets. He would petition the court for guardianship and conservatorship for both Mom and Dad. We would meet again in a couple of weeks.

Thirty-two

Before pursuing my petition to the court for custody of both of my parents, I applied for monthly long-term care insurance benefits on my mother's behalf. She had bought the policy when she retired from the Cupertino Union School District. At first it seemed that to qualify she had to be physically disabled in three physical categories, and none of these applied to her: she could bathe, dress, and feed herself. But there was a fourth category for mental disability. I filled out the forms and was told that the insurance company would send a registered nurse to interview Mom, me, and the facility in order to fully qualify her. This process could take several months.

By the time Nurse Mary arrived at the facility for the interviews, Mom had offended most of the caregivers there, so they were willing to tell Mary all about my mother's behaviors: hiding food in her room, filling her pockets with salt, pepper, and sugar packets, and refusing to enter her room until the hallway was completely empty.

The medication aides told Nurse Mary that Mom palmed her pills from her mouth to her hand and put them in her pocket. Countless pills were found in the potting soil of Mom's windowsill plants. The aides also found that Mom sometimes hoarded these palmed meds as well as the over-the-counter medications that she loaded up on when she took the facility's bus on their weekly shopping trips. Mom bought packages of antihistamines, pain relievers, cold medications, and sleep aids. The staff would perform regular sweeps of Mom's apartment looking for stockpiles of drugs, both prescription and OTC. Mom would become enraged that her meds were confiscated and given to me for disposal.

Then they told the nurse about Mom's abusive behavior

toward Dad, describing how she walked behind him down the long hallway from their apartment to the dining room. All along the way she would goose his butt and tell him to move along, saying. "Can't you go any faster?"

Nurse Mary, Mom, and I met in a conference room at the facility. Mom immediately told Mary that I had stolen all of her property.

"That's why *That* (pointing at me) will not let us move," Mom said. "She stole everything, so we have nothing left to buy a house with. We have no money at all."

I told Mary about Mom's moves and that all of her assets were accounted for.

Mary gave Mom a mini–mental state exam and she scored seventeen, exactly what she had scored at her neurologist's office. The nurse asked to see a list of Mom's medications. I excused myself. "A full list is in the nurse's office. I'll go get it and be right back."

During the time I was gone Mom informed Nurse Mary that my husband and I hated her and did things to make her miserable, that we were holding her hostage in that place so we could take her things. She said that she and Dad would get their drivers' licenses and buy a new car and travel and then buy a house, probably back in California. Mom told Nurse Mary that I threatened her, spied on her, and kept her from social activities and isolated her from her friends.

Mary and I had a conference after asking Mom to leave the room, which she did reluctantly. The nurse told me what my mother had been saying about me. I had nothing to say in return; I could only look at her and shake my head.

"You may go," she told me. "I need to spend time with your mother without you around." Nurse Mary spent six hours at the facility observing Mom and interviewing the staff.

I read the report she filed with the insurance company. It described my mother as paranoid. She had rejected all social activities offered at the assisted living facility, alleging that people there didn't like her and stole her things. The report ended,

"This woman has been diagnosed with Alzheimer's. She

is unable to socialize and spends most of her time in her room. She discourages visitors and at times the staff is not welcome. This interferes with the care of her husband, who is an invalid. She engages in erratic and irrational behavior. She has no sense of what is appropriate, therefore she is a danger to herself and to others. She will continue to decline and possibly become more dangerous as she has no thought of consequences and cannot use logic or reason to resolve her problems."

Mary's last words to me were "If your mother isn't approved for her benefits, I'd get a lawyer and sue this insurance company. I have never met a person more qualified for benefits than your mother."

During the meeting with Mary, Mom had accused Doug of stealing a wristwatch that had once belonged to her late sister Delores. It couldn't have been valuable: Delores and George had led quiet, modest lives. But one day when I was ferrying Mom around from store to store and we were stopped at a light, she had pulled a woman's wristwatch out of her purse.

"Can Doug fix this?" she asked. "It needs to have a link removed so I can wear it. It was Delores's."

Watching traffic and waiting for the light to change, I glanced at the watch and said, "Sure." She lowered it back into her purse like a spaghetti strand. It would be more than a year before I saw that watch again.

Thirty-three

The day finally arrived for my parents to be served their court papers letting them know that I was pursuing legal action: the first step in gaining guardianship and conservatorship of both of them. As Mom's mental state continued to worsen, it had become increasingly apparent that she needed this legal protection. I no longer received her bank statements, for example, as she was having them mailed to her apartment now. And there they sat, buried under mountains of purchases and old food from the dining room.

"Oh, ugh," I told Doug. "Here we go again. I was so sure that once Mom and Dad were in assisted living, with housekeeping services and caregivers and the dining room, I would never have to clean up after them again."

Mom had told the staff that they no longer had to clean her place. A horrendous odor now emanated from her fridge. She bought perfumed room deodorizers, but all I could smell when I went to their place were Dad's shitty diapers and Mom's rotting food. The room fresheners pumped formaldehyde and benzene into the room, making the atmosphere even more toxic. Mom had no idea that her many perfumed products were actually indoor pollutants. I suspected that the fumes were irritating Dad's lungs; after several bouts of pneumonia, his pulmonary system was frail.

My lawyer had assured me that when Mom and Dad were served with these papers, there would be no brutish thug jumping out of the bushes saying "You've been served!" and disappearing down the street. In our community, a retired sheriff acted as the process server. He would be gentle. I spoke with the staff at assisted living, and they also assured me that they would be nearby when my parents were served. The management was fully supportive of my petitioning the court for custody.

And it happened just that way. The retired sheriff said, "Here are some papers for you, Mr. and Mrs. McRoberts." Mom and Dad accepted them and nothing more was mentioned. My lawyer told me they had six weeks to respond to the court. They could either ignore the summons and let my petition be granted, or they could reject my petition and present their case. If that happened, then we would have to meet in court before a judge.

Nothing happened for nearly three months.

Finally I called my attorney. He told me there had been no action on my parents' part, so the judge would sign in my favor. He sent me copies of the paperwork. All good news so far—but there was an error, one miserable typo. Guardianship and conservatorship were being awarded to Karen L. Peck. My name is Karen O. Peck. I called my lawyer, who notified the court that paperwork was on the way to correct the typo.

Several more weeks passed. Again I called my lawyer. The judge now wanted a complete paper trail of my mother's assets. An annual report to the court is a required part of being a conservator. I created a spreadsheet that accounted for all of Mom and Dad's assets since they had left San Jose. I wrote, "Before that, I have no knowledge of what they did, what they earned, or how they spent it. I can only be accountable for what I know since June 2005."

More waiting. When I called again, I was told that my mother had hired a lawyer. She was fighting back.

That changed everything.

A court-appointed advocate interviewed my parents to prepare a report that would encourage the court to either support my petition or reject it. The advocate, I learned, would also investigate *me*. Any history of bankruptcy, bad credit, or a criminal record would ruin my chances of being a conservator or guardian. The advocate also required that my husband, my brother, and each of my daughters write a letter to the court stating that they approved of my action and that I was the best choice for my parents' caregiver. Any dissention among my family members would deny me the petition.

"Make sure that all of your family members agree and approve," my lawyer told me. "The last thing the court will do is concern itself with family disagreements. You have to have a solid front before the court will allow itself to get involved."

On a sunny day in autumn 2006, the advocate came to our house.

"Can I look around?" he asked as he stepped into my house. "Your mother has accused you of stealing her things."

"Yes," I said. "Feel free."

"I could get a search warrant if you require one," he said.

"No," I told him. "There is nothing to hide."

"Your mother told me what to look for."

"Yes, an old china cabinet, a spinning wheel, a couple of chairs, her mink coat…"

"Yes," he said.

"All of those things are in her storage unit."

I asked him to open all the closets and cabinets: I really wanted this whole process to be over with.

Stephanie was at our house when the advocate paid his visit. She started telling grandparent stories, the "remember when" stuff.

"Remember when we were camping and Grandma refused to sleep in a tent with Grandpa?" Steph asked. "She was certain that a snake or a bug would crawl over her."

Instead my mother had opted to sleep on the bottom bed of a camper with Kristen, in the bunk above her. Kristen was young, and such a wiggly sleeper.

"In her deep sleep Kristen rolled off the bunk and landed right on top of Grandma," Steph laughed. "We never heard anyone scream like Grandma did. And she scared Kristen, so Kristen screamed too."

"My dad laughed so hard he wheezed," I added. "He thought that divine intervention had punished Mom for not sleeping with him."

The advocate announced that he had to leave. We walked out to my garden. There were some late-season ever-bearing strawberries, and we picked some.

"I wish you could have met them when they were younger," I said. "They were quite a pair."

"Everyone who has parents like yours says that. Your mom

and dad need help. It's that obvious. I'll send you a copy of my report to the court."

We shook hands, and he left.

His report underscored that Mom and Dad needed protection.

Thirty-four

waited, much longer than I had imagined it would take, to hear from the court and my lawyer. Meanwhile, Mom was being overtly cruel to my father.

"Your mother is so mean to your dad," the assisted living staff told me almost daily.

I continued to take her shopping and to her medical and dental appointments. I stopped buying her cheap Carlo Rossi wine. Even though it had a lower alcohol content than the better wines, the sheer quantity of drugs Mom and Dad took told me that alcohol should not be a part of their daily routine. I only took Mom to stores that didn't sell it.

She, however, found a way to buy her own hooch. At least once a week the bus from the facility took the residents to local grocery stores. The facility's social director told me how much wine she bought—at least three gallons every week.

When Dad had a medical or dental appointment I would fetch his jacket from their huge walk-in closet, and I always took a moment to count the number of wine bottles that were hidden there. They were double- and tripled-wrapped in plastic grocery bags.

"The bags cover up my vino, ya know," Mom said one day. "No one needs to know my business, and I don't want anyone to see what I lug through that front lobby." One day I counted six jugs.

When she moved from San Jose to Utah, she was convinced that all of Utah was dry, so she bought cases of box wine that she found on sale. When moving day came, she worried that the movers wouldn't freight alcohol so she put the cases of wine in plain brown cardboard boxes and labeled them "kitchen." We left that wine—what was left of it—in Utah.

For me, life was both hurtling by and crawling at a snail's

pace. I couldn't believe that they'd been living in Oregon as long
as they had, yet the legal process seemed to be taking forever.

Mom's demands on me had decreased from their height in
the early days, and since I hadn't yet been called back to work,
I was desperate for projects. Doug and I cleared a small field of
weeds and scrub brush. We tilled a forty-by-thirty-six-foot spot,
bought six-by-six-inch posts for the fencing, built raised beds,
and planted a huge garden. Our old garden area was becoming
shaded by our growing fir trees, so this new one fulfilled my need
to do something physical.

I went gung ho on the garden, hauling in by wheelbarrow
tons of clean dirt and compost to fill the beds, and eleven cubic
yards of bark mulch to cover the paths between them. In my small
greenhouse I started vegetables from seed.

My dog, Maizie, and I took long walks into the forest that surrounded our place. I picked foxglove blossoms that were going
to seed and scattered them around my fields. I bought coreopsis,
peonies, and daylilies and planted them in newly made beds that I
created from dry-stacking all the rocks that seemed to grow freely
around our place. I planted maple, aspen, and willow trees for
their beauty. I went to native plant sales and bought indigenous
species for the abundant wildlife that shared our land.

We left the fruit that dropped in our small orchard for the rab-
bits and wild turkeys and other birds. We had a squawking wood-
pecker family that foraged in the trees for bugs and then savored
freshly ripened apples, sometimes knocking them to the ground
where they would be gobbled up by other browsing nomads: deer
and elk.

This was a place where I could get lost in the wildness of western Oregon. It fulfilled the longing for nature I had felt since leaving Idaho. There was no better place to be than my homestead
with my fingers buried in dirt, watching things grow and flourish
while Maizie scampered around me.

There were days when I'd rather have the flu than go to town
and be with my parents. They were pretty much as rehabbed as
possible, both medically and dentally, but they still needed me
regularly. Mom called me every day, and each time I heard her
voice, I cringed.

Thirty-five

Once again the holidays rolled around. We were "celebrating" by repairing extensive damage to the laundry room from a leaky clothes washer, when my attorney called.

"Your mother's attorney says that she has never been invited to your house."

Well, yes, that was a true statement, but ...

"It's more than a two-hour round trip to take Mom from assisted living to my place and back again," I said. "You have a copy of my calendar. Just when am I supposed to do this? And how can I bring my mother to my house and not my father? Mom has refused to let Dad come along."

I also told him that we had actually planned on having Mom and Dad over for that year's Thanksgiving, but our house was presently torn up because of our soggy laundry room problem..

"Everything is a mess. I worry about my dad tripping, and how am I supposed to fix a big meal while we're rebuilding our laundry room?" It sounded so lame and defensive, but it was all I had as a rebuttal. Not to mention that it was all true.

Once again we went to a swanky restaurant in town for Thanksgiving. Mom and Dad ordered several strong cocktails, but that night I didn't care about their alcohol consumption.

We managed to wrap up the repairs and brought my parents over for Christmas. Kristen came as well. I dreaded the moment my mother would enter the house. It had been seventeen years since she had been in my home, dating back to Kristen's high school graduation.

"Your eggs are stored wrong," she had told me then as she inspected my tiny home in California. She had strolled from room to room, finally opening my fridge and finding eggs in the open tray on the door instead of in their carton or a plastic box. "They'll absorb refrigerator odors. And things stored on the door are warmer than if they're actually inside the fridge."

After cleaning up her filth and toxic waste multiple times and moving her from San Jose to Utah to Oregon, such remembered criticisms filled me with rage. If she stayed true to form, I couldn't wait to pounce on her and invite her to leave, to tell her this was *my* house and as humble as it was, I loved it.

"This is very nice," Mom said instead. She quietly walked around the place, looking at my walls and walls of bookshelves, the comfortable chairs and couch, and low lighting. The house was filled with the luscious aromas of our Christmas feast. "This is very nice, Karen, so comfortable, so cozy."

I was shocked into silence.

"May I have a glass of wine?" she asked.

Hell yes, I thought, *have the whole bottle.* Pure satisfaction and joy ran through me. My mother had paid me a compliment! I immediately felt ridiculous; I was sixty years old, soon to be a senior citizen myself, and still seeking her approval. It felt silly to gush, but maybe I was just relieved that Mom hadn't taken out her pile driver and pounded me into the ground with her hurtful, cutting words. That would have depressed me for days.

We ate a lovely dinner. Mom's glass kept being refilled. Dad kept hitting the wine as well.

As the conversation wound down and the after-dinner lethargy set in, Dad said, "Lila, it's time to go."

Mom glared at me and said, "You're trying to get rid of us, eh?"

"Grandma," Kristen said, "that was Grandpa who said it was time to go. Mom didn't say anything." Kris's words had no impact on Mom; she sat in hostile silence.

But it was time for them to go. I packed them some leftovers, including a couple of slices of pumpkin pie with whipped cream. Kristen and Doug drove them to their apartment while I did the dishes and put things away.

Thirty-six

The staff at assisted living had promoted me to the position of "Dial-A-Daughter," as they never had to take Mom or Dad to any of their medical or dental appointments. I was still unemployed, taking a couple of classes at Oregon State University, thinking of applying for a master's program or at least completing a second bachelor's degree since I had so many extra credits.

In early February I asked Mom and Dad if they would like to get out of their apartment for a while. It had been a very cold, icy winter. Normally in our part of Oregon, winters were quite temperate, but this one was harsh and Mom complained of cabin fever. She refused to use the area's free community transportation for the elderly and disabled.

"Each ride costs forty dollars," she told me.

Where did that come from? "Mom, it's free. All you have to do is call them."

As usual, she was convinced that she was right and I was wrong. Instead of arguing with her, I offered to take her and Dad to the local Shari's for lunch.

"Oh hurry up, Jim," Mom said as she jabbed his butt with her umbrella.

It had been a while since I'd had to help Dad in and out of a car. I rarely took him anywhere since Mom bitterly complained about his presence. He shuffled along, grimacing and panting with each feeble step. Right away I noticed that he had gained weight and it was difficult for him to move in any direction. He couldn't lift his legs. Once his butt was planted on the passenger's seat I had to hoist each foot onto the floor mat and then strap on his seatbelt. This brought me very close to his face, and I noticed a lesion on his nose. I made a mental note to get him to his doctor.

There was a freezing wind that robbed our bodies of heat.

Even layers of fleece and windbreakers couldn't stop the relentless gusts from making us shiver. But we'd be okay if we didn't dawdle outside.

I dropped Mom and Dad off at the front door of the restaurant, then escorted them inside to make sure they were out of the wind while I parked the car. They sat on the bench near the entry and waited for me.

I walked behind Dad as he followed the waitress to our table. He ordered salmon—something he'd rarely had when Mom was cooking, as she hated all seafood. She ordered a steak, and I ordered a salad. Mom kept her eyes on other parts of the room. When she glanced at Dad, she sneered, "*That's* pathetic. I can hardly stand *It*," pointing at him with her thumb.

As usual, Dad's ninety-two-year-old nostrils were filled with a perma crust of dried snot. His face was crisscrossed with scars from all the skin cancers that had been removed. His skin was zit-plagued with pustules and blackheads. His poor old head was bald and small and spotted like Mr. Burns's on *The Simpsons*. No one grows cuter as they get as old as Dad. His lower eyelids sagged outward, looking as if they could almost turn inside out. The beauty Mom said she had fallen in love with had disappeared.

I asked for to-go boxes for what they didn't finish. Dad said that he had to go to the bathroom.

"Mom, I'll take Dad to the bathroom. Please ask the waitress for the check when she comes by."

I escorted Dad down a long hallway to the men's room. I knocked and no one replied, so I opened the door and helped dad over to a urinal. I left so he could do his thing. I stood outside in the hallway listening for noises that would signal that he was done. There was no way he could maneuver his walker and open the door at the same time; if he stepped backward he could lose his balance and fall.

Fortunately, there were no other gentlemen in the bathroom, so as soon as I heard Dad moving around, I opened the door. His eyes were focused on the floor, and the front of his pants was soaking wet. I helped him over to the entrance and sat him down on a vinyl-covered bench. I saw other people noticing Dad's wet pants—they looked away instead of meeting my eyes.

"Wait here, Dad," I said. "I'll go get Mom. Then we can leave and you can change your clothes." I pulled his jacket down to cover his stained pants, but customers continued to stare and then look away.

Hurrying back to the table, I found Mom examining the dessert menu.

"Mom, you were supposed to get the check from the waitress," I hissed. "Dad has wet pants and we have to go."

The waitress came by at that moment. "My mother would like the chocolate mousse—to go, please—and I need the check. We'll meet you at the cash register."

I put my arm under Mom's elbow and hoisted her to her feet, then helped her on with her jacket. At the cash register I told her, "I'm going to get Dad into the car. You wait over there for your dessert and I'll be right back."

I ran out to the parking lot and drove my car to the entrance. The temperature had dropped even further, and I could only imagine wet clothes meeting up with that cold wind. I helped Dad shuffle out of the restaurant, got him into my car, and buckled his seatbelt. I was grateful that Doug and I had made it a policy that any time Dad rode in one of our cars we would always have his seat fully covered with beach towels over a layer of plastic.

I met Mom at the cash register, and once again she was looking at the dessert menu. I asked her if she wanted anything else. "We have your leftovers and your dessert, but we can get another dessert if you'd like."

I realized that Mom's day out had been hampered by Dad's incontinence, but I also realized that he was sitting in my cold car on one of the coldest days of the year. At long last, she was ready to go.

On our way back to their apartment, she asked me to stop at several grocery stores.

"Mom, we stopped at three places yesterday, and you're not out of anything."

Once we were back at the facility I asked the staff to help Dad get out of his wet things and into the shower.

"Mom, let's go get a cup of coffee."

I took her to Starbucks, knowing that if she were out of the facility she wouldn't be able to interfere with Dad's care. He would be clean and shiny when we returned. I bought a couple of extra mochas so he could have one too.

It seemed there wasn't a moment in any of my days when I failed to think up horror stories about how Mom could put Dad in harm's way. She was like a wasp hovering around his face, ready to sting him for any and all transgressions, real or imagined.

"I cannot get anything done with your dad around." She repeated the familiar mantra. "All he does is sleep and watch TV."

Fully recognizing the futility of it, I said anyway, "If Dad is sleeping then he's not interfering with your activities. And once again, this is *assisted* living, so they could tend to Dad. You're paying for these services, so you might as well use them."

She waved her fingers in the air.

Thirty-seven

On the legal front, things were at a standstill. A week after Dad's accident at Shari's my lawyer informed me that Mom's lawyer wanted a second opinion.

"He says that you've tainted your mother's medical records. He agrees with what your mother says, that she doesn't have Alzheimer's, that you just want her to have it. Since your mother's neurologists are the only ones in Corvallis, she'll have to go outside the area for this second opinion."

I shouldn't have been surprised. More than once she had told me, "You *want* me to have Alzheimer's. If I have it it's only because you *want* me to."

I had no idea how to respond to such a ridiculous claim though. She had been diagnosed after a thorough examination, an MRI her neurologist had ordered, several office evaluations, and MMSE testing.

For reasons unknown to me, my mother had long been terrified of this disease. When she was in her seventies and still healthy she had told me, "Kill me first, Karen. Just kill me. I don't want to be one of those la-la land people. You make sure that I'm dead."

I finally found words to respond to my lawyer. "Yes, Mom has told me that she thinks I've influenced her doctors."

"And how do you respond to her?" he asked with raised eyebrows. "I don't think I've ever heard of someone wishing Alzheimer's on another person."

"I told her that I would never do that. But this disease terrifies Mom. She panics at the thought of being incapacitated. Possibly one reason is that she thinks it's one more thing my father will make fun of. He has stroke-related dementia himself, though, so he's not even aware of her condition."

This new requirement of a second diagnosis posed a dilemma.

There was no one who could take Mom to another city for a neurological workup, and her lawyer wouldn't allow me to drive her,
lest I taint his all-important second opinion.

Eugene and Salem were each an hour away, Portland two
hours. Sending Mom off alone in a taxi would be careless. So we
waited until Mom's lawyer came up with a plan that assured us
that Mom would be escorted by someone who could open a door
for her, make sure she ended up in the right office, and then get
her back home again.

I knew she needed an escort because of what I'd seen repeatedly. Each of the dozens of times I had taken her to the same dentist's office, she headed in the wrong direction when she got out
of the car, even when I parked directly in front of the office door. I
always had to take her elbow and guide her to the entrance.

When I voiced my fears about Mom getting lost or disoriented
to my lawyer, he always had the same message: "Karen, for you
to prevail, your mother has to fail—and you have to let her."

I knew this. I knew I had to let my mother reveal to the world
how fragile and inept she was. I had to be quiet and let her show
her stuff. Still, I feared that the court would deny my petition if
there was no second opinion and I would lose my case because we
lacked evidence. Would the day come when I'd get a call inform-
ing me that Mom was out there alone in the predatory world?

At times she was credible, but I knew the full story. From
cleaning up after the filth, chaos, and financial mismanagement
that their lives had become, I knew that she and Dad were in need
of protection—and that Mom's idiot-for-an-attorney was not her
go-to guy. It was stunning to me that he was so willing to disregard what the doctors said and put her directly in harm's way.
And promising her that she was perfectly capable of living independently again was mental cruelty. She would fail as she had
in San Jose and in Utah. She was failing now in assisted living in
many ways, but at least she had some support, care, and protection.

My legal limbo continued. I kept calling my attorney, urging
him to contact Mom's attorney about getting that second opinion.
I knew her diagnosis would be confirmed. By then she was on a
higher dosage of Aricept, a common Alzheimer's drug, and the

dosages of her antipsychotic drugs, Risperdal and Seroquel, had been increased three times.

On several occasions Mom's neurologist had asked her to list all of her drugs, their dosages, and the purpose of each. The staff at assisted living had also asked her the same questions about Dad's medications, since she insisted that she was capable of administering them. She had been unable to tell anyone a thing about her or Dad's medical conditions, what they had, and how it was being treated. But Mom and her lawyer were insisting that she was capable of living independently and taking care of Dad! I was beyond angry.

The facility kept accurate records of all of Mom's medications. If her ignorant attorney really wanted a second opinion, all he had to do was grab a pharmacist, walk into the nurse's station, and ask to see her drug sheet. Aricept, Risperdal, and Seroquel are powerful drugs that are only given to those who absolutely need them. I was frustrated beyond belief that her attorney would not take even this small, easy step. He seemed hell bent on declaring her competent.

I had copies of the reports on Mom and Dad the facility kept in its files. Every resident was required to have a service plan and have it updated regularly. This plan determined how much care my parents were to receive, and it was also used for billing for those services. I shared the notes with my lawyer.

I asked him to urge Mom's attorney to contact the facility office and do some homework so he could see for himself that my parents were not good candidates for independent living. They were too old, too ill, too fragile to be on their own. But even if that information made it to her lawyer, I was coming to realize, he probably wouldn't react to it or bother to do the follow-up research. He was Mom's paid whore, apparently determined to get her whatever she asked for as long as the purse strings remained open.

"She's paying him thousands of dollars," I said to Doug. "He could at least pretend to care about her safety."

Mom's lawyer finally decided that she would be re-evaluated at our local mental health clinic; the testing would be conducted there by a psychologist in mid-February. I was highly skeptical that a shrink would be able to perform all the tasks necessary to accurately measure Mom's brain health, but I had no say in this endeavor, and I was pleased that at least some progress was being made. And I was relieved that she wouldn't have to travel very far.

The day of her evaluation, the receptionist at Mom's facility called. "Your Mom just returned from the mental health clinic. She's very disoriented. She's upset."

The next day I stopped by and invited her to lunch. We went to a restaurant that had delicious soups and baked goods. She was clearly still shaken, and I asked her what had happened.

"I didn't know how to fill out the forms. You know my medical history better than I do—why didn't you take me? I couldn't remember the building I was in or why I was there. And then they asked me about your father's history. He's tough as nails. He'll last forever. What do they need to know that crap for?"

"Mom, your lawyer set this up. I wanted to be with you, but he said that I had to leave you alone."

"It sure was awful having to go to that doctor by myself. What was her name?" The name wasn't all she'd forgotten. She didn't recognize that the clinic she had visited was right next door to her primary care physician's office—she thought it was in another town.

It was several weeks before she regained her composure and once again demanded that she be able to move. She seemed certain I was the only thing standing in her way.

"Mom, if you truly understood your circumstances, you would know what you can and cannot do. You shouldn't have to depend upon me, nor should you have to ask me about anything, especially your ability to conduct your own life."

"You're not our guardian?"

"No, Mom. Not yet anyway. I'm still petitioning the court, but you and your moron of an attorney are opposing me."

Her lawyer had promised mine that the results of Mom's second opinion would be shared with us. By March he was still refusing to offer us a copy of it.

❖

Every time I entered my parents' apartment there was something new in it, something cheap and ugly that Mom had acquired. Her good taste had deteriorated from Stickley and a personal decorator to worthless junk. The day after my lunch with Mom, I got a call from the receptionist at the facility.

"Karen, hi." She paused. "Your mom just received ten boxes from UPS today. They're all pretty big. Things are piling up in her apartment. The staff doesn't know how to clean her place anymore, plus she won't let us in in the first place … and there's an odor."

Great. Mom had discovered the joys of mail order, and her hoarded food stank. But she insisted that she was A-OK.

"I am not your prisoner," she had told me repeatedly.

"No, you're not," I'd agreed.

"This place is a jail."

"No Mom, it isn't. But it's very telling that you think it is and that you think you have no personal freedoms."

Worried that there might be something awful in Mom's apartment, especially the rotting food, I devised a plan to sneak in when she was either out of the building or out of her room and see if I could take care of it. I hoped to find a copy of that second opinion as well.

Knowing when Mom and Dad would be in the dining room for lunch, I chose that time, and I entered the building from the back so as not to be seen. Mom often forgot I had a key to her apartment, and that day I used it.

There was a stack of paperwork and mail next to the phone, and near the top was a letter from the psychiatrist who had interviewed Mom at her lawyer's request.

I had a hard time focusing my eyes. Words like *dangerous, paranoid, dementia,* and *fear* kept on popping off the page. In the closing paragraph the doctor wrote, "Lila, I fear for your safety and the safety of your husband if you try to live independently."

So once again—now from a fourth professional source—there were those unavoidable words. Mom is a danger to herself and to others. And her stupid attorney was still telling my lawyer that Mom could make it on her own and care for her ninety-two-year-old husband.

In the same pile I found paperwork from moving companies. One had given Mom an estimate of over thirty-five hundred dollars to move her and Dad back to San Jose. I also found old invoices that hadn't been paid. I found a letter from her attorney asking her to pay her bill. I smiled at that one, but I couldn't linger. Once I got home I could copy what I found and return the original documents later.

I visited Mom and Dad a couple of days after my raid. Mom was holding an obviously cheap piece of pottery in her lap. "What's that?" I asked.

"It's an American Indian artifact."

I took it from her and looked at it. "It says 'Made in Vietnam' on it. Why do you buy this junk?"

"It's for my new house in California."

"So you're moving?" I asked, probing for more information.

"Yes. My lawyer tells me that I'm fine and I can resume my normal life."

"Did he read the letter your doctor sent? The one from this second-opinion doctor?" I knew that her lawyer had a copy as the one I read was cc'ed to him.

"Oh, things are fine. I passed all my tests with flying colors."

Red flags were dancing in my head. I asked the staff to be on the lookout for any signs Mom was trying to act on her plans.

It didn't take long for the phone to ring. "Karen," Angie said, "your mother just left with a stranger. She refused to sign out, and the man she left with didn't leave a business card. Your mom thumbed her nose at us when we asked her to sign the sign-out sheet. Guess she doesn't want us to know where she went."

Mom eventually returned, and the staff asked her escort for a business card. He was a representative from a moving company. I called the number and said that my mother had Alzheimer's, that I had power of attorney, and that there was a court case pending for full custody of her. "I will call whoever is necessary, even the police department, if you try to move my parents."

Eventually I would have to contact seven moving companies, all of whom backed off. But that did not deter her. She spent hours thumbing through newspapers and yellow pages searching for someone who was willing to truck her belongings south.

"She'll find someone if she keeps this up. I worry that once she's run through all these legitimate companies she'll find a predator," I told my lawyer.

I was on a first-name basis with every moving company in our community. Their administrative assistants called me on a regular basis as Mom continued to contact them. They were wonderful at making up stories to convince her they were interested in her move but were just too busy for her now.

"Hi, Karen. Your mother called us again this morning wanting a date for her move. I told her that the university students moving back into town hogged all of our trucks, but maybe next month we could fit her in. Do you have any word from the court yet?"

"Ah, no. I called my attorney this morning, and Mom's attorney still says she can live on her own. He won't let us settle unless I back down. But we're still pursuing full custody."

By this time I was working as a senior technical writer again. I received calls at work daily about my mother's behavior. I knew all of the taxi services and called them regularly, just to keep in touch and remind them that my mother could not be their customer.

I often cried all the way to work and all the way home, a sixty-mile round trip. On the job, I lost myself in huge, long-term projects that took every ounce of my concentration. I took on more assignments than any reasonable person would ever consider. At one time I had seventy-five projects to complete, but the work kept me sane, giving me an outlet for the perfection I needed, an antidote to chaos. I was in control of this structured environment, and each project had a happy ending—unlike my life at the moment.

All I heard from the legal world, time after time, was that Mom's lawyer said she was competent and she would never grant consent for me to be her guardian.

Mom told her lawyer that I had forced her to surrender her driver's license, so I produced the form she had signed when she willingly surrendered it while requesting an Oregon ID card. Then her attorney wanted to personally see if all of her possessions were in the storage unit as I had claimed. I gave my attorney the padlock key and pass code so an inventory could be conducted. When it was complete, her lawyer sent a letter to mine admitting that all of her possessions had been accounted for.

In March 2007 my husband was gone for a week on a business trip. Assisted living called.

"Karen, your mother is complaining about her windows."

"Windows?"

"Yes. She wants them all replaced. She says they make it easy for her to be watched."

"Watched? She's on the second floor. Someone would have to be very tall to be able to spy on her."

"Yes, that's what we said. But she wants her windows removed and replaced."

"OK … I'm not sure what to do, but I'll talk to her. I mean, even if the windows were replaced they would still be clear glass. I hope she can understand that."

Around that time I thought about making an offer to her attorney. Maybe if I tried to meet him halfway we could come to an agreement. Mom was adamant that she and Dad return to San Jose. I was against it if the plan was that they live independently. But if they could live in an assisted living facility, then maybe they could return to California and still be in a protected environment.

After all, it really didn't matter if Mom and Dad lived in Oregon or in California. It was most important that they be safe and that their needs be met. Maybe if Mom was back in California in a familiar place she could socialize more instead of indulging her retail therapy; the few friends she'd left behind could visit her. I realized I would be more than willing to move Mom and Dad back to California if it meant I could be rid of her jerk of an attorney.

I called six assisted living places in the Bay Area, asking if Mom and Dad could move there. Each facility gave me the same response. "Since your mother has a diagnosis of Alzheimer's and your father has vascular dementia from his strokes, they cannot move to our facility. If they lived here prior to that diagnosis and then became Alzheimer's or dementia patients, we could not evict them—they could stay until we could no longer meet their needs. Then we would recommend a memory-loss care facility. But since they have already been diagnosed, we cannot permit them to live here. We're just not equipped to take care of them as they decline further. We only offer assisted living, and your mother could still come and go as she pleased. All assisted living facilities are at-will places—there is no lockdown, and lockdown is what your mother needs for her own protection."

If there was any chance at all for my parents to move back to California they would have to be in a memory-loss facility and probably live separately, mostly to protect Dad from Mom. But Dad had panic attacks when Mom wasn't around. She made it plain that she wanted him to pass away, but he couldn't live without her.

Separating Mom and Dad had been a fantasy of mine when I was a child and couldn't stand their constant fighting. But they had stuck together for more than sixty years, and now there was a dependency they were too old to change.

After hearing her say, "If that bastard had any decency at all he'd just die," almost every time I spoke with her, I finally couldn't resist asking her why she had stayed with Dad for all of those years.

"Mom, when Greg and I left home you were still a young woman, only in your late forties. You were educated and had a good-paying job with benefits. If you had to sell your house to settle with Dad, real estate was still cheap—you could easily have afforded a smaller house or a condo for yourself."

She waved the question away.

"Mom, it seems to me that you wanted what your mother had."

"What's that?"

"Your mother had twenty-five years of widowhood. Your dad was in his sixties when he died. Your husband is in his nineties. I suspect that you have waited and waited for Dad to pass away so you could have the house, the assets, and the country club membership and not be labeled a divorcee.

"There were certainly good reasons for you to leave him. I mean, coming home and seeing my husband choking my daughter would surely send me to divorce court."

She was quiet.

"I'm just trying to understand why you've stayed with him."

"I didn't want to be a divorced woman. Staying with your dad made things easier, like the country club, buying a house and cars, and taking trips. Who ever thought your father would live so long?"

Yes, Dad smoked and drank for years and years and so did Mom. His consumption of tobacco and alcohol was quite impressive, and they should have done some damage. When I was a kid Mom used to make me wash her windows, walls, and ceilings. They were filthy with smelly brown goop from those cigarettes. It was a disgusting job and I hated it, but that's how much they smoked. It was enough to dye the interior of their house a brownish-yellow color that had to be washed off.

Dad's strokes should have killed him. When he fell he sometimes smacked his head on the floor or a corner of the fireplace. His bouts of pneumonia also should have killed him. He had skin cancers everywhere from his long days on the ski slopes or the golf course. He was an awful driver, but others seemed to watch out for him. His foul temper should have blown an artery. But Dad hung in there, eating heartily and waking up each morning to my mother's ire.

Mom, too, should have perished. In the early 1990s she had an aneurysm on her aorta. She had been playing golf and felt like her chest was congested, but she insisted on finishing her game. Afterward she went to her doctor, who sent her to the emergency room. She had open-heart surgery immediately, and during the operation she had a heart attack. But she pulled through and was golfing again in a couple of months, and she finally quit smoking—only because after the surgery it hurt to cough. One of her sisters died of lung cancer when she was in her sixties; Mom was lucky to survive six decades of smoking.

Eight years later she was having a routine colonoscopy and there was a bowel perforation. The mortality rates for this are very high, but Mom was patched back together and now, while we were having this conversation, she was in her late eighties. Year after year Mom and Dad lived on, and now they were back in my world. Dad's dementia isolated him—he could no longer drive or move about freely—but he loved the staff at assisted living. He was in the dining room for every meal. The director of the facility loved hearing his stories about Idaho, the railroad, and golfing. And Dad still loved to flirt.

He developed a sizeable skin cancer on his nose. Mom was disgusted by the way it bled and oozed. I took him to an ear, nose, and throat surgeon to get it removed. As the nurse lowered Dad to a fully reclined position, he had problems breathing. The nurse raised his bed until he was more comfortable.

"You all right now, Mr. McRoberts?" she asked.

"Yes dear," he said, "I'm fine. You walked into the room and took my breath away."

I told Mom about this later, and she just sneered. She had a way of raising her upper lip over her front teeth to fully express her disgust. She was often disgusted: when she wore lipstick her teeth were streaked with red.

So here they were, my parents, living in my territory. Neither one of them was healthy enough to move again and neither one was capable of fully comprehending their situation. All they wanted was what they could no longer have: an independent life, a life from twenty or thirty years ago. But that life had been then, and I was dealing with now. After talking with six assisted living facilities in the Bay Area, it became clear to me that all options for Mom to move again were closed.

I gave my attorney the list of names, addresses, and phone numbers and the contacts I had spoken to about moving my parents back to California. He passed it along to Mom's lawyer. Her lawyer never responded, so I never knew if it even registered with him that Mom and Dad had run out of options: they could never live independently again. It was now obvious that the only choice for Mom and Dad was to stay in Oregon under my supervision. I would have to continue to fight this legal battle, pursue it until it could no longer be pursued. I had no idea what the outcome would be, and none of the lawyers involved seemed to be in any hurry to resolve it. I had set up residence in legal limbo.

Thirty-eight

All Mom's attorney seemed to care about were her possessions and financial assets. Her physical and mental welfare were of no concern to him. One day my attorney called me on my cell phone while I was at the grocery store. Doug was on a business trip.

"Karen, your petition for custody of your parents is turning into a criminal case against you."

I hung on to my grocery cart, thinking I'd fall to the floor if I had nothing to support me.

"This is very serious," he continued as I stood frozen in place in the paper products aisle. "Your mother and her lawyer are accusing you of stealing all of your parents' assets. This is a felony that can carry jail time and huge fines. And your petitions to the court will be soundly rejected if there is any truth to this."

"Y-You have to understand," I stammered. "This is all imaginary. My mother is very paranoid right now. And she desperately wants to move again. When I tell her that we won't help her move she interprets what I say as that she *can't* move, period, and she blames me for stealing her money and making it impossible. She can actually pack up and go at any time—I don't have to tell you that—although, as you well know, I'd be first in line to try to prevent that for their own safety."

I went on to explain to him that Mom had been telling the caregivers at her facility, who relayed this information to me in private conversations, that the reason she couldn't move was that she was penniless and had no resources to facilitate a move.

"The truth is, Mom is incapable of making any viable plans, and I think she knows it. Telling herself that she's lost of all of her wealth to her thug of a daughter makes her my victim instead of the victim of a disease that terrifies her. It's how she digests her diagnosis—denial and accusations."

I paused and let my lawyer think this over. "Bring me a list of all of your parents' assets," he said. "A spreadsheet that shows what they sold their houses for, where that money went and when, and where their investments are now. I need it first thing tomorrow morning. We can't wait on this, Karen."

That night I combed through all the financial records I had. It was now April 2007. The previous autumn my lawyer told me she was now under her attorney's protection. Now, my lawyer insisted, I had to keep out of my parents' finances. Now I'd lost sight of their financial activity for about six months. And meanwhile, Mom had convinced her attorney that I was the poor, needy daughter who coveted other people's resources.

This was insane. Doug and I earned around a hundred fifty thousand per year. Our mortgage was paid off. We never carried any debts, and we had managed to put away a big chunk for our retirement *and* take expensive vacations. As I assembled what records I could, my teeth were grinding, and I had a headache.

Mom's money was important, for their future and their quality of life. Without it she and Dad would have nothing. Greg and I had agreed that it would be lovely to have an inheritance, but mostly we wanted to protect *our* wealth from Mom and Dad. If they went broke, we'd feel obligated to help them, at least keep them from becoming homeless. I was determined to stay very interested in my parents' assets. And Oregon has filial responsibility laws that state that indigent parents must be taken care of by their eligible children. If we didn't offer financial support to care for our parents, Oregon law could force us to do so.

When my attorney first told me to butt out of my parents' financial records, I argued that their paperwork had been a royal mess, and it had taken me months and months to straighten it out. I tried to paint a picture for him, describing the disarray I had found in 2004 when Kristen and I cleaned out the garage at their San Jose house. Stacks of bank statements tucked willy-nilly throughout the house. Huge unpaid credit card bills. All the cash stuffed in places they might never look again. I *had* to help organize and protect their assets.

When their mail had come to my house, I kept things neat and tidy and paid their bills on time. I wrote checks from Mom's accounts to pay off an eleven-thousand-dollar debt to Visa and thousands more to Sears and Mervyn's. Then I cancelled those charge accounts and permanently opted out of all credit offers. It took a huge effort to stop all of the junk mail come-ons, but things had been running smoothly.

I had wasted my breath arguing; my lawyer insisted I had to wash my hands of all of it. I was no longer allowed to pay any of their bills, including the monthly payment to the assisted living facility. Their medications were billed separately, and I couldn't pay that one either.

I wasn't entirely forthcoming though: there were some bills Mom and her attorney didn't know about. I had kept the life insurance policy her mother had purchased for her back in the 1930s a secret. The death benefit was less than seven thousand dollars, but I didn't want it to lapse, so I paid the fifteen-dollar premium myself.

I had also kept Mom's long-term care paperwork coming to my house. Her diagnosis of Alzheimer's put her in the mentally disabled category and qualified her to collect sixty-five dollars a day, around two thousand dollars every month. As soon as her monthly check arrived, I deposited it into her bank account and kept the receipt. After a couple of months, I set it up for auto deposit into her checking account.

Now, facing the prospect of a criminal investigation, I figured I'd better clue my attorney in. When I met with him the next day, all the financial records I could get my hands on in tow, I stressed the value of these benefits and why I especially didn't want to risk a lapse in long-term care payments. If Mom actually managed to move and live independently, she would lose this monthly benefit; she had to live in a licensed facility to continue to receive it.

"Again, Karen," he said, "you have to let your mother fail. It will be good for her lawyer to see the financial mess she can make. And if we have to face a hearing, the judge will want to look at her finances as well."

This advice made my head throb; that was happening a lot lately. Cleaning up after Mom had been a Herculean task. I simply wasn't willing to let her create crisis and chaos again—knowing that I would be the one to clean up, again.

The news didn't get better. "Karen," my attorney said, "your mother has also accused you of other things. She says that you've never let her into your home, that you abandoned her when she had open heart surgery, and that when everyone thought your father was dying of pneumonia you refused to see him. And she's saying you have a history of asking for handouts, that you were a 'welfare queen,' to use her term, and a bum while you were raising your kids."

Not knowing how to respond to any of that, I said nothing.

"If any of this is close to being true, a judge will frown on your petition. We may have to consider hiring a caregiver for your parents. Maybe they could pay someone to be their guardian and your brother could watch their finances as conservator."

I had had just about enough of this insanity and I finally found the words. "I can refute each and every one of these statements. Mom is simply trying to assault my character, and her pocket-lining lawyer is probably urging her to do this. My mother is *para-noid*, for crying out loud—what do you think the antipsychotic medication is for? She *makes things up*. I can only guess what's underneath it all, but I think deep down she's trying to shelter herself from me and what I'm trying to do to protect her. She's terrified of Alzheimer's, and if I win this legal battle, she won't be able to deny that she truly is a very sick woman with a fatal disease."

My attorney nodded, but seemed unmoved. "There's more. There's a missing watch that belonged to your mother's sister. Your mom says your husband stole it."

I was silent as our meeting wound down and my lawyer told me how he planned to handle my host of predicaments. When I returned to my car, I was seething. It took several minutes to compose myself to drive—road rage would only add to my stress. What a nasty person my mother could be! Underlying my fury was heartbreak. It was clear now that my mother had few feelings for me.

Mom was Mom, and she had always been treacherous. If I hadn't trusted her in the past, I certainly couldn't trust her now—

especially with the truth. Her illness was ravaging her. I knew I had to rise above this, to be the better person, take the higher ground, and do my best to ignore her comments. I had no control over what her legal weasel thought either. I had to believe in my own goodness. And I had to stay true to my goal: protecting these old people from themselves. Even if I hated her at times for her crushing behavior, which hurt me deeply, indulging in such emotions would gain nothing.

And deep down, I also sympathized with the woman who tormented me. I knew that her six decades with Dad had been loveless, that he had verbally abused her, that he had cheated on her. I could also see that as Dad's health had failed, she had gotten the upper hand and become the abuser—and that in her determination to punish him for his wrongdoings, she was also harming herself.

The day after meeting with my lawyer, I got a call from assisted living.

"Karen, your mother fell today. She's all right. The nurse checked her out, and she's fine. We faxed her doctor, and he's OK'd a prescription for Tylenol with codeine. But she's in a foul mood, and we're worried that she could be mean to your Dad— well, meaner than she normally is."

During my lunch break I picked up Mom and took her to Starbucks for coffee.

She wasted no time explaining her fall. "He peed all over the floor. He gets up in the middle of the night and wanders around. He peed on the floor, and when I had to use the bathroom I slipped and fell in it."

While she spoke, she avoided looking at me.

"Geez, Mom, I am so sorry." And I *was* sorry for her.

All I could do was to continue to fight for their safety and protection. The newspapers were filled with reports about missing dementia patients and the predators who robbed and beat them and sometimes sexually abused them. Mom and Dad deserved to be safe.

At least Dad was happy, or seemed so, when I asked him how he liked living as he did. "I like it here just fine, dear." He liked Oregon, he liked our cars, he liked the food, he liked the staff, and he liked sleeping in front of the TV with a golf game on.

Mom was different. Earlier in her life she had found things, people, and places she liked, but the older she got the more sour she became. In San Jose she had hated the Asians who moved into the neighborhood. In Utah she had hated the heat: "It's too hot. Everyone stays inside. You can't meet anyone because of the heat." And now she despised assisted living. "We want to move. The food is lousy here, and the place is filled with people who are in la-la land."

Despite her approval of certain people and things when we were growing up, neither my brother nor I could remember a single moment when she seemed truly happy or even momentarily pleased. With Mom, it was always nagging and criticism. And now she even talked about how much she had hated Sun Valley and L.A., places she hadn't seen in years and had once claimed to love.

Mom hated Dad but wouldn't live without him. Dad couldn't live without her. So on and on my fight went as I tried to protect the two oldsters. And now one of them was fighting back, tooth and nail.

My report of all of Mom and Dad's assets had been as complete as I could make it. They were all in Mom's name, dating back to when Dad had his strokes in the 1990s; after his recovery, she didn't bother putting things back into joint ownership.

After Mom sold their San Jose house the money went into an annuity she purchased in Utah. When they moved to Corvallis I had asked the Utah branch of the company that managed the annuity to forward the paperwork to the Corvallis branch. I had assumed that it was done. Then, with the money from the Utah house, Mom had bought two more annuities. They could access this money at any time through a monthly allowance and not pay penalties, and until that time the annuities would earn interest.

I labored over my spreadsheet, and when I was done I found that Mom had diminished her wealth considerably. Her move to Utah had cost almost seven thousand dollars. She paid more than forty thousand dollars in real estate and escrow fees. Her move from Utah to Oregon cost more than five thousand dollars: even though Doug and I did the actual moving, we had to rent a truck and trailer to tow our car and pay for our expenses. When she sold her Utah house she spent twenty-five thousand dollars in real estate and escrow fees. I had written checks from her account to pay off almost twenty thousand dollars in credit card charges, and they had to pay more than thirty-five thousand dollars in capital gains taxes because they sold two houses in one year. Then she was performing her favorite trick—blowing through her bank account by buying and hoarding things she would forget even existed.

Mom's fortune of almost nine hundred thousand dollars was now down to just over seven hundred thousand dollars. If anyone was pilfering Mom's money, it was she.

Now Mom had more than fifty thousand dollars in her checking account and just over ninety thousand dollars in a money market/savings account. Between their pensions, Social Security, and long-term-care checks, Mom and Dad's income was close to five thousand dollars a month. This covered their expenses, so with careful management they wouldn't have to depend on their investments to meet their financial needs—at least not yet, until the expense of assisted living increased and demanded that they draw on their assets.

When Mom and Dad first moved to their facility, Mom had insisted that I have my own key to their apartment. Once in a while when I dropped by to visit them and knew they'd be in the dining room, I'd cook up a ruse so I could snoop and see if I could head off further financial disaster. "I have to use the bathroom. If you don't mind, I'll use yours and see you in your room after you're done eating."

My attempts to find financial information were not always successful though, because of Mom's propensity for "filing" her records inside junk mail and in the garbage Usually, I could only glean a few hints of what Mom and Dad were doing with their money, as I was always afraid of Mom walking in on me. My investigations were short and less than thorough.

My attorney understood that once I was asked to leave their financial affairs alone I couldn't be held accountable for all those months I wasn't privy to their information. I felt a bit of relief hearing that. But the accusation of felony theft still made me squirm.

"What about their taxes?" my lawyer asked me during one of our many meetings.

"I've been filing for them. They have a CPA in California—I gather their information and send it to her and she does the tax work. I write the checks to pay her. Mom and Dad have owed no taxes for years, nor do they get a refund."

When I had asked Mom if she was doing her taxes or if she had someone in mind she said, "You take care of it. You seem to know so much more than I." As incongruous as this seemed given her obvious distrust of me, Mom realized the importance of filing a tax return so she freely allowed me to enter the secretive world of her finances. She had no objections when I said, "Mom, I really need to look through your mail for your 1099s for your taxes." Combing through her paperwork gave me some insight, but that opportunity came infrequently.

When she let me have her checkbook so I could write a check to pay her CPA, I could quickly glance through the register and the carbon copies of her checks. All that stood out were checks written to vendors of Mom's newest collections of worthless items.

My attorney quietly reviewed all the paperwork I had supplied. I had included a copy of the letter from the psychologist who had evaluated Mom: that precious second opinion her lawyer had claimed would prove that my mother was a capable of caring for herself and her ninety-two-year-old husband, buying a house, and living a structured and safe life. The letter clearly indicated that Mom would be in deep doo-doo if she tried to live alone again with Dad.

I could have saved myself some copier ink. "Karen, we can't use this. It would violate HIPAA privacy laws. Unless your mother specifically allows her medical records to be entered into court as evidence, which will work against her, you can't introduce any of your mother's medical history. You could be prosecuted for committing a felony if you do." Another threat of a felony charge. I was not in the least bit encouraged that I could continue this endeavor.

If we had a court hearing and Mom spoke for herself, she had to be the drooling village idiot before the judge. But if her attorney spoke on her behalf, her true mental state would never be revealed. If I couldn't offer the court Mom's medical records, it seemed my case was doomed.

For several weeks after this revelation, there was silence from the legal world. Meanwhile, at work I received more phone calls from moving companies telling me that Mom was still hounding them. All I could tell them was that I was working with my attorney to get a resolution to the case. I realized that Mom was wasting their time, taking them away from other customers who were fully qualified to use their services. It was frustrating, but I was powerless to change the situation.

One day, a banker I'd worked with at Mom's bank called me. "Karen, your mother is here with her attorney. They're looking for her annuities. We have no record of that one for two hundred and fifty thousand." Then she lowered her voice. "Karen, her lawyer is insinuating that you stole this money . . . And Karen, this guy is a real creep, a real poser," she whispered.

It was clear now that my request to transfer the annuity from the Utah branch of this bank to Corvallis had not been honored. I left work early, dug in my records for the policy number, and called the banker with it. Then I called my attorney and told him what had happened.

"Good, yes, good that you called," he said. "Your mom's attorney already phoned me. He's rattling my cage about indicting you for financial abuse of a senior."

Things never quieted down where my mother was concerned. I did receive a copy of my attorney's letter letting Mom's lawyer know that the annuity was intact and had finally been transferred from Utah to Oregon. But I still received calls from assisted living every week letting me know that Mom was delinquent in her monthly payments. The director knew that Mom's attorney had demanded I stay out of her financial affairs, but he was trying to run a business.

He did offer an option: he could help Mom write her checks to the facility, and all she would have to do was sign them. (Apparently, the first time she had tried to write a check on her own in the director's presence, she became embarrassed; she went through three checks before filling one out correctly.) But this was a scary prospect. If someone trustworthy could talk Mom into writing checks, it could just as easily happen with someone who was up to no good.

I knew the director was right about Mom's inability to fill out a simple check. Before her lawyer came into the picture, I had taken her shoe shopping. She needed a pair of comfy walking shoes, and I knew of a store in Corvallis that carried the brand she liked. They were on sale, so she decided to buy two different colors. She started filling out her check at the counter. There was a *Dilbert* calendar next to the cash register, and she began making the check payable to "Dilbert." The gentleman behind the counter was polite enough not to laugh, but he had to bite his cheek and look at the ceiling.

"Hey Mom, why don't you let me help you with that," I offered. I filled out the check and we left.

Week after week it seemed as if I were spinning around in a hamster cage. Mom's attorney once again demanded a key to the storage unit. Mom insisted—again—that I had stolen all of her things: the old china cabinet, her mink coat, her antique lamps, all the things she treasured that wouldn't fit into her apartment.

Again I dropped off a key at my attorney's office and gave him the numeric code to get through the gate. And again a few days later he called and told me all of Mom's things were accounted for. I seemed to be in a storage unit *Twilight Zone.*

"So let's get this straight," Doug said. "Her dipwad of an attorney already went into storage and verified that all of her stuff was there. That's not good enough? He thinks you stole all the stuff out of storage, then moved it back for his inspection? Maybe he's the one with dementia!" I had to laugh at that, and it seemed like my first good belly laugh in months.

"But it's all billable hours and travel time for that idiot, so maybe he's not so dumb, this Mister-Pocket-Lining-Lawyer," Doug said.

The next day the owner of the storage place called me to tell me that Mom had called him twice that day.

"Karen, your mother keeps asking me when I'll be at her

apartment to pack up her things. She thinks I'm a moving company, and she thinks we have a signed contract for me to move her to California."

Thirty-nine

On a cold April morning I went to pick Mom up and take her to a checkup with her neurologist. My lawyer wanted to know what the doctor's advice was concerning her request to move back to California. Although we couldn't submit her medical records to the court, we were able to make note of her doctor's comments to me.

"Hey, Karen," the receptionist asked as I signed in, "have you seen your mother yet?"

"No, I was just going to her room. She has a doctor's appointment this morning."

"She has your dad's tooth, and she won't give it back."

"Huh?"

"At breakfast this morning a tooth fell out. Your mom grabbed it and put it in her pocket. The nurse checked your dad's mouth, and she thinks he's in pain."

I shook my head—it seemed there was no limit to how strange things could get. "OK … I'll try to get Dad in to the dentist today."

At the neurologist's office we talked about Mom moving. "Absolutely not," the doctor told her. "You would be foolish to try to live on your own. And why would you? You have a very cushy life—your daughter takes care of everything and the place you live in is plush."

Mom turned away from her.

The doctor spoke to Mom's shoulder. "I have to tell you. You're not shackled to your daughter—you're a free woman. If you want to move, then move. I'm just telling you it would be both foolish and dangerous. I don't advise it, and it concerns me that you don't seem to realize your true status as a person who still has rights. And you don't seem to be aware of your condition. Every time you come here you deny that you have Alzheimer's."

With that she began running her through another MMSE. With the first question, Mom looked my way, wordlessly asking for a prompt.

The doctor caught this. "You can't help her with this test, Karen. No hints, no head shakes, no clues at all."

Mom had always been so good at denying the truth, and attempting to create her own. Lately she was telling people that I had given her Alzheimer's. When I asked her why she would do that, she denied having said it—she lied about lying. But here in the quiet of the neurologist's office, the truth about her condition was like a fourth person in the room.

Mom was failing the MMSE at almost every step. Her humiliation was profound, and there was no escape. I moved out of her line of sight. She seemed to relax a bit when she couldn't see me watching her.

I had been so angry with her. Everything she said and did hurt or incensed me so much that I often could feel no compassion for her at all. But as I watched the testing proceed, the truth in the room cut through the many layers of resentment and disappointment I had built through the years. No matter what had happened in the past, right now my mother was very, very sick. I was exhausted by a lifetime of coping with her games and deceit, but there was no point in carrying baggage that only served to further sap my energy.

I had to soften. It was time for me to understand that my manipulative mother was now very ill with a devastating and terminal disease—the very one she feared most.

I had been acting in the best interest of my parents all along, but I had felt the victim all the while and had somehow clung to that. It was time for the mother-daughter pissing contest to end. I had to let her irrational, insensitive behavior flow on by as I moved forward with their care. I had to detach from it. I knew my future with my parents held further upsets and struggles, but no longer could I afford to wear my resentments like a cheap, secondhand cloak, wrapping myself in it as if it were something of value.

❖

I will always be amazed by how good Mom was at hiding her condition. Whenever she became aware that she was saying or doing something inappropriate, whenever she felt cornered by the truth, she changed the subject, cut a conversation short, or made a physical exit from the uncomfortable situation. She had always been clever at turning the tables, putting anyone who displeased her on the defensive. If I touched on a sore subject, she went on the attack, suddenly looking me up and down, for instance, and saying, "Hey, how much do you weigh now?"

I tried not to get sucked in, but after comments like that I just wanted to be away from her; being on the receiving end of such insults was exhausting. For her part, she never seemed to tire of it—she was constantly at war with someone. She liked, then hated my Dad's family. She liked, then hated every place she had ever lived. She liked, then hated almost every person in her life except for her birth family. Them, she adored, and she was miserable and lonely after they all passed away.

Despite our painful history I realized now that I could feel sadness for Mom's plight and the future she had to face. Memory-loss diseases do not crest instantaneously. Patients who suffer from them don't lose everything all at once. They know that things aren't right. They know that empty space is invading a territory that once was theirs, and it's terrifying.

They might react with sadness, anger, paranoia, or any other response in the range of human emotion. There are thousands of stories about Alzheimer's patients, and all are different. The only common thread is that they're all slowly dying of a fatal disease. The real tragedy of Alzheimer's is that the brain goes first, leaving the body to struggle without the support of the mind.

My brother and I once talked about these diseases and our own potential for being plagued by one of them. We agreed that we'd prefer a heart attack, or being hit by a bus, or dying of exposure while climbing a mountain. At least those are relatively quick. Alzheimer's can last for decades. If a person has good physical health while the brain goes missing, the anguish of Alzheimer's will plague a family for a long, long time.

Mom scored a fifteen on her MMSE this time. This put her in the middle stage of Alzheimer's.

"Lila," said the neurologist, "this test score tells me that you're on the low end of brain function. You cannot drive and you cannot consider living by yourself. Your daughter is doing all the right things."

To me, she said, "You should sue her lawyer. He's emotionally abusing her, promising her things that will never happen."

She turned back to Mom. "If this mess you're creating ends up in court, I plan to tell the judge that you are best cared for by your daughter."

Mom didn't know that such testimony would be inadmissible unless she signed a release, or that asking people with a mental illness to sign any legal document is a tricky business; it can be invalidated quite easily if there's a hint of mental impairment. All I could hope for was that the doctor's words would carry some weight and that Mom had not yet lost her respect for, and fear of, authority figures.

On the way back to the facility I asked Mom about Dad's tooth.

She put her hand in her pocket. "As soon as we move back to California I'll let your dad see a dentist." Somehow, in my mother's mind, my father's tooth was leverage.

I had called our dentist from the neurologist's office and scheduled an appointment for Dad for that afternoon. It looked like I'd be missing almost a full day of work, so I called a coworker to let her know. I would voucher my hours as paid vacation—again—and that was disappearing quickly. Doug and I were giving up hope of having time off any time soon.

We were also giving up hope of staying healthy ourselves. I had bronchitis five times within two years. Maybe it was from inhaling all of the dust, dirt, mold, pulverized insect remains, and toxic chemical fumes from each of Mom's moves, or perhaps it was the stress from everything that was happening. My thyroid was starting to fail, causing me great fatigue; it took almost three months before my thyroid medication kicked in and helped me feel somewhat normal again. I had bouts of irritable bowel syndrome, enough so that I knew the location of every public bathroom in the county. It helped to eat bland food, but even so, time spent with my mother could cause many, many trips to the ladies' room. Sleep was frustratingly elusive. I kept a stack of books on my nightstand so I could read my way through the night. The days' events that took me away from my desk meant I had to work harder and put in extra hours to get my projects done on time, which led to more sleepless nights and a deeper state of exhaustion.

Even Doug, a truly healthy guy, was getting colds and flus, illnesses he had never suffered in our many years together.

Before Mom got out of the car, I asked her to give me Dad's tooth.

"The dentist said that he has to have it for Dad's appointment this afternoon." I knew she really liked our dentist (so far at least). "I'll have to tell the dentist that you have it and won't give it back."

She handed me a paper napkin that was rolled into a ball and taped shut. Mom had written on it, "Jim's tooth, April 2007." I put it in my purse and thanked her.

Before leaving assisted living and rushing to work to get a few projects done, I asked Dad to open his mouth as wide as he could. I saw that an upper front tooth was missing. Each time he inhaled through his mouth, he winced.

"Dad, breathe through your nose and your tooth won't hurt so much. I'll be back to take you to the dentist this afternoon."

On my way out the door I turned and held up the taped napkin ball. "Hey, Mom, were you going to put this under his pillow for the tooth fairy?"

Suddenly she began to giggle. The angry lines that had been etched on her face since I'd known her vanished, and for a few minutes, I watched my mother laugh.

Dad's "tooth" was actually a crown that had fallen off during his morning meal. The dentist polished it up and glued it back into place. I sat across from my father while the dentist and his assistant patched him up. I noticed that his ankles were huge, bulging over the tops of his socks, wider than his feet. His frail old heart could no longer pump away the fluids that pooled there,

and apparently the diuretics he took weren't enough to compen-
sate. Mom hated that he took diuretics: "They make him pee all
the time."

I drove Dad back to his apartment listening to his deep, hacking cough as he attempted to clear the mucous that filled his lungs.

Doug and I commuted to and from work together during this time.
In the mornings we chatted quietly and talked our way through
our projects so that by the time we reached work, we both had a
good idea of how the day would flow. On our long drive home,
we had the opportunity to vent about the workday. Usually, by
the time we reached the quietude of our front door, we were
purged and ready to begin our home lives without the specter of
work-related problems infiltrating our personal domain. That day
was different: I couldn't shut up.

"Can you believe that Mom's *piece of shit* lawyer says they can
live on their own? Mom can't even provide Dad with *simple dental
care*, and Dad had *no idea* who to call—he kept saying he was all
right. The director is hounding *me* to get my parents to pay up.
They're behind thousands of dollars and they're being charged
late fees. And that jerk of a lawyer wants them to live independently. He says I *interfere!*

"You should see their apartment. There's just a narrow path
through the bedroom to the bathroom. The staff can't clean in
there anymore—Mom won't let them in! The fridge stinks. Dad
can hardly walk. Now Mom wants to move to Idaho. Sure, fine,
great!—I can just see Dad in fifteen feet of snow. And that asshole
of an attorney thinks Mom can be Dad's caregiver? He's *been* to
their apartment. Does he think things are normal? He's seen the
letter from the psychologist. His blasted second opinion is even
more damning to Mom than the evaluations from the long-term
care nurse and the neurologist. That letter should send shivers up
his spine. The doctor of *his* choice has confirmed that Mom is bad
news on her own and she's bad for Dad too and that *bastard* wants
them to be protected from *me!* Who the hell is going to protect
them from *him?*

"OK, so maybe I can't stand either one of them, but I take good care of them. And I made sure that their lives would be well managed—at least they eat, and they live in a safe environment. That bastard wants to send them out into the world on their own. And he tells my lawyer to tell *me* to butt out of their lives? *I'm* the one who's supposed to be a criminal?!"

On and on I went, and Doug chimed in with his own complaints. We both went to bed frustrated, impatient for the legal world to face reality and move my petition forward. We slept badly and woke up cranky the next morning.

Doug tried to shine a little light on the morning. "Just remember, sweetheart, in a couple of weeks we'll be going to Ashland. Personally, I can't wait for a dinner at Macaroni's." And this reminder did brighten the day. Vacations had been scarce during the past few years spent contending with my parents' lives; it was wonderful to know we had one coming up in the near future.

Finally, in April, one of the legal shoes dropped. The court awarded me full guardianship of Dad. It issued no conservatorship because he had no assets in his name, but the guardianship was a big step in the right direction.

"I can still tie Mom down, you know, by keeping Dad at the facility," I told my lawyer.

"Well, Karen, that plan will work as long as your dad is alive," he said. "Once he's gone, you have no hold on your mother."

Even more reason to keep Dad safe.

For the rest of April and into early May, I visited my parents a few times. Mom was in a horrible mood. She snarled at the staff at every opportunity, and the moment she saw me she launched into a barrage of complaints: "I hate the food here and the coffee is awful and every day they serve fish, every day, and I hate fish. I'm allergic to fish. And your Dad's bum needs to be wiped all the time."

"Mom"—it did no good, but I couldn't help trying to counter her complaints—"please let the staff help with Dad. These people are trained to deal with incontinence. It's why they call it *assisted* living. You certainly pay the bucks for these services. And they don't serve fish here every day, and even when they do they always have at least two other entrees to choose from."

"No. Your father would be embarrassed if someone else saw his messes." She didn't try to argue about the fish. I had known for years that her "allergy" was a myth, ever since she had eaten a tuna salad sandwich at my house thinking it was chicken.

I asked the staff whether they tried to help Dad when he messed his pants. "Sure we do. He's fine with us helping him, showering him and changing his clothes, but that's only when your mother isn't around. When she's here and we try to get into her apartment to help him, she has a fit. She gets so upset that *he* gets upset and starts yelling too. She tells us that her lawyer won't allow us to help him."

By then I was ABBY as far as my mother was concerned: anybody-but-you. One day she had asked me, "Are you my guardian?"

"No, Mom," I replied. "But I'm trying. My petition is still before the court."

"Well I'm still fighting back. I don't need a guardian, but if I did, it would be any-body-but-you. A-B-B-Y. I'm calling you ABBY from now on."

I was used to the name-calling. All through my childhood it had been something: knucklehead, dummy, whatever other insult was handy. Lately I had been Dial-a-daughter and Jailer. Now I could add ABBY to the list.

What she couldn't see, of course—and would probably have refused to see even if she were capable—was that being her de facto guardian was my own jail sentence. I was just as shackled as she was, tied to her like a guard to his prisoner. I had to be the ever-present brick wall she ran into whenever she talked about moving or acted on her plans. Yes, her neurologist had been correct in pointing out that Mom didn't fully realize she was a free woman, and that this was another indication that she couldn't see the real world. But that was only half the picture. Even as she complained of being held captive, she had been busy on the phone, actively pursuing her escape. One day she could outsmart me and disappear.

Forty

Day after day, Mom still combed through the yellow pages searching for moving companies to hire. She preferred to stick with the well-known companies, and these were the ones she called weekly, sometimes daily. As ever, they then called me, and I let them know I was still trying to become her guardian.

I was beyond grateful for the understanding and generosity of the staff at these places. To help me in my efforts to protect her, they continued to use clever delaying tactics. Mom didn't have enough belongings to fill an entire truck, so she would have to wait until someone else came along to share it with. Or all the trucks were out on the road moving other people. It was clear they were as fearful as I was about the prospect of a nearly ninety-year-old woman with Alzheimer's wandering out into the harsh world, easy prey for scams and abuse. They, too, could envision her disappearing without a trace. They were angels in disguise.

Mom's lawyer never knew how many hidden connections I had made to keep her safe. In addition to moving company staff and cab drivers, I had dozens of contacts inside the assisted living facility. Mom confided in the activity director, and this kind lady would call me afterward or we'd meet in a room at the facility where Mom couldn't see us. I knew she was watched constantly by people who had her interest at heart. Still, I couldn't relax; Mom was the most determined person I had ever met.

I had to be good to her—my conscience wouldn't let me lash out at her as I had done before she became so ill. And there was another reason I couldn't be anything less than compassionate: if I said anything negative to her, she would tell her lawyer and my legal suit would be toast. She was making up enough stories about me, stealing and mistreating her; I couldn't give her any ammunition that was actually true. But oh! She could make me so angry.

One day I took Mom to Mervyns. Dad needed new socks, pajamas, and pants. He was gaining weight now, and he could no longer zip up his trousers. His hand was constantly in the candy bowl, kept amply supplied by Mom. He ate every dessert offered to him at the dinner table, and he never missed a meal. Aside from Mom's forced marches up the hill outside their apartment, he never exercised.

Dad's diabetes wasn't serious enough to be treated or even monitored. A registered nurse provided foot and nail care, making sure that there were no open sores or ingrown toenails. He was, however, retaining fluids at an increasingly alarming rate. His bloated feet told the tale of how bad his health was.

On the way home I broke the news to Mom. "You can move," I told her. "You can move any time you want, and you've always been able to do that. But Dad can't. The court awarded guardianship to me and he's not moving. He's too fragile. Dad is under my protection for the rest of his life."

"He's tough as nails," she retorted.

"No, Mom, he's not. He's ninety-two. He can hardly walk, his feet and ankles are balloons, he sleeps all day, and he's not lucid. He can't even shave anymore. He can't bathe or dress himself. He called you by his father's name the other day, and yesterday he couldn't remember *my* name. He's old and he's endured two huge moves in the past two years. He's not moving, but go ahead and help yourself. Just remember that even though all of the assets are in your name, Dad is legally entitled to half of them. If you want to leave badly enough, then divorce him. Half of the assets will be yours, and you can do what you want."

Her defiant, angry mood abruptly changed to one of defeat.

"Well then. I guess that's that. I can't move without him."

"Mom, it doesn't have to be so bad for you here. There's a small golf course nearby, you know. Our community has tons of services for seniors. There are all those places I've already taken you to see. You can still have a life if you just get out and start socializing again. Leave Dad to the caregivers here at your place. Go have some fun. I'll go with you and help you meet new friends."

It was wasted breath. I had taken her to see the local golf course I'd mentioned many times. They told her they had a ladies' group made up of elderly women. The eldest was eighty; Mom was eighty-nine—not too far off. They played nine holes once a week. I reminded her about it. "I'll take you to the golf course and pick you up, and maybe even play a few embarrassing rounds myself until you get used to the place."

There was also the Corvallis Community Center, a beautiful facility that offered day trips for seniors, dancing lessons, swimming or wading at the public pool, and so much more. Every month I had picked up its calendar, hoping that Mom would find something irresistible, that she would get out and find a friend.

"Mom, there are so many women at assisted living. Certainly there's someone for you to be friends with. I met a lady in my Alzheimer's support class. Her mother and you graduated in the same class in Minneapolis. She's right here in the same facility as you."

"Oh, I already know about her. I never liked her much, and now she's in la-la land," Mom said, waving away the thought.

I had taken her to all of the antique stores, thinking she might enjoy volunteering. Her knowledge of lamps and fine furnishings was impressive. "Nah," she had told me. "I don't want to be a clerk."

"Doug and I donate blood several times a year to the Red Cross. After we're done donating there are these little old ladies who give us juice and cookies. They chat away and seem to enjoy it. You could do that. You used to love to socialize."

"I have no interest in donating blood."

"It's not about donating. It's about volunteering for the Red Cross. You know you're too small to donate blood."

"I said no. I don't want to donate blood."

It became a familiar, disturbing dance: I found ideas for her entertainment and she found excuses to refuse. But I continued to hope for a different outcome.

Her neurologist had shed light on the problem. "Your mother is paranoid, Karen. She'll find any excuse she can to remain a recluse." The antipsychotics and antidepressants didn't seem to be working. Every time I saw her she seemed more desperate, like a caged animal seeking an exit. She could no longer just stroll down the hallway to the dining room; she scurried with her arms tucked against her ribcage and her hands wrapped around her waist, and she was always looking around to see who was following her or watching her. She never made eye contact anymore; her gaze always scanned the surroundings. Her erratic and irrational behavior kept all of us around her holding our breath. I navigated as best I could, but the plain truth was that she terrified me.

"Your mother has left with a stranger again, and she refused to sign out," the receptionist said when I answered the phone.

Several hours later, the phone rang again. "Your mother found a moving company outside the Corvallis area. That's who she left with. When she returned, one of the housekeepers went out to the parking lot and asked the man for his business card. I'll leave it at the desk for you."

I picked up the card on my way home from work and called the moving company rep. Mom had asked him for an estimate to move her things to San Jose. She hadn't been able to remember how to get to her storage unit, so he had found it for her and added the contents to the estimate. He had no idea that he was dealing with an Alzheimer's patient.

I told him in broad strokes about my legal case and that the court was deciding about conservatorship for her. "If we win, my brother and I will control her estate. You need to know that we won't release funds to pay for a move that will be harmful to her and my dad." This happened several more times with other moving companies. Each time, Mom managed to appear competent long enough to get a bid. Each time, I had to recount the painful truth.

"Karen, there's a taxi here to pick up your mom. We told him she was unavailable," said a voice on the phone one day.

I called the taxi company and offered to pay any fees. I explained that my mother had been diagnosed as a flight risk, an "exit seeker," and that we were working with the court to try to get her protected.

These kinds of calls came with increasing frequency. Each time, I reminded her that I wouldn't let Dad move. And each time, I called my lawyer to tell him that Mom's plans were escalating.

The legal machinery seemed to have ground to a stop, and I called my brother in frustration.

"Next time you visit your lawyer, look at his watch," he told me.

"Am I looking for a Rolex?"

"No. Instead of numbers it'll have months. It'll read January, February, March instead of one, two, three. The legal world moves very slowly."

One afternoon while I was at work, my lawyer called to tell me that he and Mom's lawyer were going to get together. Her lawyer fully understood that I would never let Dad move and that I would use my guardianship of him to keep Mom anchored, if I had to.

I asked my lawyer if I still had power of attorney for Mom. Her lawyer had provided her with the forms to fill out to revoke it, but the last time my lawyer had checked with the courthouse, nothing had been filed. Mom seemed to know that a POA couldn't keep her from moving, but a guardianship could.

As a result of my legal efforts, it was clear that she both feared and hated me. But that didn't stop her from calling me almost every day and making demands on my time and energy.

After a miserable time in a store where Mom seemed to need everything on every shelf in every aisle, I was reduced to telling her that I was leaving and she could find her own way home. She gave in, and we left together with half of the things she wanted. She had bought three stuffed animals because they were on sale.

I tried to refrain from rekindling the same old conversation, but I was too tired to resist. "Mom, you buy and buy and buy this cheap crap. It fills your apartment, and you never open anything or use anything. Your dresser in your closet is so buried you can't get to anything in it, including Dad's clothes. No wonder you both wear the same clothes every day and they're dirty."

"I know things about you that I could tell," she said, her eyes focused on the dashboard. "I know your history and it's none too pretty, let me tell you."

"What?"

"You've been married *three times,* and you were a bum of a mother on *welfare* and you had *no job* and you flunked out of school and you drank and smoked and who knows what all else. I know things about you that I could tell the world."

I could feel myself losing control. "Well, Little Missy," I said. "I know plenty about you that I could tell too. You drugged me with alcohol when I was little so my coughing wouldn't disturb your husband. You stayed with that same man after he tried to *choke* me. You made me walk home from school with a broken arm. I flunked out of school because Irene was killed by a drunk driver, which you and Dad did all the time, drank like fish and then tried to drive home with Greg and me in the backseat. Believe me, I know way too much about you, so don't you *ever* try to pull that bullshit with me."

I pulled up to the facility, got out, and opened her car door. "Get out," I barked. I slammed the door and watched her hurry inside. Only then did I realize I was shaking.

We had done so much for her, and the mistakes I'd made in my life were ancient history. I had been happily married for more than twenty-five years. I had accomplished so many good things: I was a wonderful mother and the best wife. I had graduated from Oregon State University magna cum laude. I was a superstar at technical writing. After a rocky start growing up in an unhealthy home, I had figured things out and become the person I had always wanted to be. How dare she throw the past in my face after I had sacrificed my own life to help her and Dad? Her threats had made me more miserable than I had thought possible. I was deeply wounded.

I had lost all those days, the ones when everything is perfect: the house clean, the yard work done, the bills paid, the fridge full. Doug and I loved each other and our kids and our jobs and our life. But once I stepped into my parents' lives I couldn't seem to remember those days, my perfect, happy days.

After our kids moved out, Doug and I had enjoyed years of uncomplicated living. Each year we chartered a sailboat and explored the San Juan and Canadian Gulf Islands. We went to Europe, did wine tastings, bought season tickets to the Portland

Opera and the Portland Broadway series, spent weekends in Ashland or went camping and hiking. Or we simply stayed home and relaxed and enjoyed one another's company.

There had been a time when I could add one more perfect day to a long list of other perfect days. I gazed out onto our well-groomed yard, admiring its beauty as the birds and wildlife roamed close to our house. I inhaled the aroma of rosemary turkey slowly roasting in the oven. My husband and children were healthy and successful. The cars were paid for. I sat in my favorite chair and was filled with gratitude for my life. Would I ever make it back to days like that?

I knew I had to stop my pity party, draw a deep breath, and focus on the fact that no matter what I was sacrificing for my parents, I had volunteered for this project. There was no one named Jailer in my life. I had to honor my own commitment to take care of them, and in doing so I had to fully understand that my life couldn't be all about me for a while, maybe for quite a while. I could cry and complain and feel stabbed through the heart, but that wouldn't help me take care of these two old people who were so obviously incapable of fending for themselves.

So it was shut-up time for me. There was no point in resenting what I couldn't change; Lila and Jim McRoberts were very old and very unhealthy. I was able bodied and smart. These were the realities of my life.

A wave of shame washed through me. I had let Mom push my buttons, and I had responded to her in kind. I took a deep breath and renewed my promise to treat her with compassion. Given our history, it seemed a foreign idea. But given her illness, I had to keep trying.

v

Forty-one

As Mom became more paranoid, our relationship became even more contentious. After the terrible confrontation in front of the facility, having threatened her and ordered her out of my car, I felt hideous. I went immediately to our local wellness center and made an appointment to see a counselor: I needed a new set of coping skills.

I couldn't allow myself to get so angry with Mom. Or at the very least, I couldn't let her see my level of rage again. I had truly wanted to hit her—just one good punch—and that alarmed me. Mom was barely over a hundred pounds, and she was shrinking, quite literally, and I'd had to resist the urge to get physical with her.

I had enough awareness to know that this feeling was primitive—it was the lizard part of my brain that wanted to strike out and coldcock her—and that it was pent-up hostility seeking release. But she was eighty-eight and I was sixty: what glorious headlines that would have made.

There comes a time when regret for an action comes at a higher cost than any short-term reward merits. In the long run, the only reward I could ever reap was to know I was doing the right thing.

"Whatever I do will either haunt me or comfort me later on in life," I told Doug. "The last thing I want for myself, for us, is to regret. Mom regrets her entire life. I don't want that, ever. Regret turns to hatred—I've watched it happen to her. I don't want that either."

I hoped the wellness center would help me learn how to cope when Mom pushed my buttons. I didn't want anger to be my default emotion when I was around her. Though I knew it wasn't in the cards, how I wished we could be like the other mother-daughter pairs I saw who held hands and smiled at one another, looking like they'd been best friends since conception.

My daughter Stephanie had a dog named Luna. She was as human as any dog can get, a big mixed breed, more than eighty pounds and every ounce of it pure love and happiness. There were times, though, when Luna could be a naughty girl and had to be scolded. For example, eyewitnesses swore that at a wedding reception, perfect-dog-Luna nicked a chicken breast off a serving table: the evidence was gone in three swallows. We didn't catch her that time, but we had our eyes open for her next mischievous act.

In Luna's ninth year she was diagnosed with osteoscarcoma in her shoulder. "No matter what she does from this point forward, she will never be in trouble again," Stephanie decided. "She will never be a naughty dog. From now on she can do no wrong. She is not to be disciplined. In her last days she will know only peace and love."

Learning from my daughter, I became determined to apply the same attitude to my mother. She was not to be scolded, only protected, from herself and from predators on the elderly. Keeping her out of trouble had to be the most important thing. And maybe, just maybe, keeping her out of trouble would also protect my fragile father.

I spent two hours with the wellness counselor, telling her everything, pouring it all out. When I had wound down, she had this advice: "It's all right for you to get angry with your parent. You have to allow yourself permission to feel your emotions."

"That's it?" I replied. "That's all you can offer me? I actually know it's OK to get mad. I really do know that, about permission and such. I need something more than that, something more substantial. I need a whole new set of coping skills."

I stood up. "I guess I need to look for it elsewhere." I left and never went back.

While I did find some comfort with a local Alzheimer's support group, I burst into tears the moment I started speaking. And then I couldn't shut up. I hogged all the available time telling my miserable stories, and then I felt awful that I wasn't offering any support to the others.

I learned some valuable things from that group, though. I discovered that when Mom bought all of those bottles of salad dressing, it was probably because they reminded her of happier days. I also learned how to abruptly change the subject when things got tense. "Just walk over to a window and start talking about the weather or some such bland subject," I was advised. "Pink roses, for example. She'll calm down and forget what she was saying to you." These little tidbits were a help, but between work, my home life, and my parents I was cramped for time, and eventually I stopped going to the meetings.

However, they led me to other resources, including a list of highly respected memory-loss care facilities in our area. I toured two of them. They were quite similar, but one was closer to our house and our lives so I decided on that one. I didn't want to have to make another hasty decision, to wait until another crisis like the Utah debacle presented itself.

Their assisted living facility was top notch, and I had no regrets about moving my parents there. And Mom had asked me to do just that. A move to a memory loss facility, though, would not involve her permission. I filled out an application and got her name on a waiting list. They gave me a form for her primary care physician to fill out, and I went through the motions.

Though I knew it would be the best I could do for her, the thought of putting Mom in such an institution was disturbing. Doug and I walked around in a state of numbness, not wanting to plan anything or go anywhere. Finally we realized that we were both severely depressed. We were watching our savings being devoured; we had written checks for almost nine thousand dollars in legal fees. Our paid vacation time was also drying up.

Working four ten-hour days, we had regular three-day weekends. We looked forward to our upcoming, although brief, getaway. The Oregon Shakespeare Festival in Ashland was one of our favorite destinations for short weekend trips. The theater was inventive and original. The motel we liked had a swimming pool. At nearby Mount Ashland we could hike along a leg of the Pacific Crest Trail. Ashland offered great restaurants, shopping, and a dog park that our Maizie loved.

We talked and talked about our upcoming trip, clinging to

that glimmer of relaxation and relief. We had taken our last real vacation so many years before that neither of us could remember when it was, where we went, or what we did.

Forty-two

Mom and Dad had checkups scheduled with their primary care physician. Though the exam room was cramped, he saw them both together. I stood by. I had written the doctor a letter letting him know about my mother's many attempts to move, and that I was now my father's guardian.

"We want to move and she won't let us," were my mother's first words to her doctor. "She's taken away everything from us."

"Mom, Dad has dementia and you have Alzheimer's," I said. She became enraged at this. She stood up to slap me but I took a step backward and she missed. This was the same thing she had tried to do before in this doctor's office.

"Do you hear what she says about us?" Mom said to Dad. "Do you hear that?"

The doctor and I stepped outside into the hallway.

"She seems more aggressive toward you. Are things getting worse? I've seen her try to hit you before."

All I could do was nod.

"I'll sign that referral to memory loss care. We have to protect your mother—she's completely irrational."

All the way back to their apartment, Mom would not let up. I turned on the radio. Every time she launched a verbal attack, I turned it up. There wasn't anything I could do to get her to be quiet.

I escorted them to their room. As I was leaving, Dad said, "We don't want you here anymore."

The sign-out book at the front desk blurred as I filled in my name. I cried all the way home. Dad was nice to me now; we got along. It had felt sweet finally being able to be his friend after all our conflict; it was such a welcome change. All of my negative feelings about my father had dissolved when his strokes overcame his foul temper. We were buddies now.

His words rang in my ears: "We don't want you here anymore."

I was feeling such loss, a kind of broken-heartedness that was new to me. But I had to acknowledge I shouldn't have been surprised this had happened. Mom and Dad's ties to one another had always been perverse. Despite their history of mutual betrayal, whenever they felt threatened by someone else they became a tightly knit team, pulling up drawbridges and setting out the alligators. Even when they had both been healthy, there had been no hand holding, no tender words, no other expressions of love. There had been, instead, only an indestructible connection that was nearly primordial in nature: *it's you and me against the world, and to hell with how we feel about each other*.

Forty-three

I t was Friday, May 11, 2007, our big day to leave for Ashland. We had reserved three pairs of tickets to the Shakespeare Festival. I packed just about everything I could find in anticipation of all the other activities we could enjoy: two cashmere sweaters for dinners out, boots for hiking, swimsuits for the motel pool.

"Your suitcase is like a box of tampons," Doug joked. "You can go swimming, play tennis, ride a bike ..."

I pretended to ignore the comment. "We can hike around Mount Ashland. We won't need to take Maizie to the dog park if we wear her out on the mountain. There should still be some snow up there for her to roll in."

I closed the suitcase by sitting on it and zipping it up between my legs. "Listen," I said. "I will not start my vacation with a smartass, so you be nice to me."

For that I got a kiss. We started loading up the car.

Doug had gathered road food from the kitchen. Our dog had taken her pre-trip pee break, and I had crammed the last bag into the car. We came back into the house to do a security sweep: windows locked, doggy door closed, heater off, no appliances running. Doug put two bottles of water into the small ice chest. He smiled and said, "Let's go."

We were so outta there.

The phone rang. We stood motionless, looking from it to each other. Caller ID told us it was my parents' assisted living facility. I let the call go to the answering machine.

"Hi, Karen. It's about your dad. He fell this morning. We think he needs to see a doctor. He has a lot of lower back pain, and it's hard for him to move. He says it's uncomfortable to breathe. It's not an emergency, but he should be checked out."

All our hopeful excitement about the trip evaporated.

217

It was mid-morning. I called Dad's doctor to make an appointment. He wasn't in the office on Fridays, but there was an on-call doctor available. Dad could see her at four-thirty that afternoon. I returned the call to the facility and let them know we'd be there to pick up Dad for his afternoon appointment.

Silently Doug and I unpacked our suitcases and emptied the ice chest. Doug hung up the dog's collar while I called the Shakespeare Festival and cancelled our tickets.

"I hope someone can take advantage of those great seats," I said.

We sat in our living room and watched TV, occasionally checking the clock to make sure we allowed enough time to pick up Dad and get him promptly to the doctor's office. It often took more than half an hour to get him ready and in the car.

We ate the peanuts and drank the water that had been meant for our trip.

Just past three o'clock we drove the familiar thirty miles to Mom and Dad's place. We parked under the large portico out front. In the apartment, Dad was sitting in his recliner. His breathing came short and loud—he was almost panting. Clearly, he was in a lot of pain, much more than we expected.

"What are you doing here?" Mom demanded.

"We heard that Dad fell and he needs to see the doctor," I said.

As usual, she avoided eye contact and turned away. "Well, you certainly get around."

"Yep, Mom. I'm the eternal social butterfly."

"Oh, he's tough as nails," Mom said. "He'll be fine tomorrow." I moved closer to Dad and tried to assess his condition.

"I've had to wait on him hand and foot all day. I even had to carry a food tray for him so he could have his lunch here in our living room instead of the dining room down the hall."

"Mom, you pay top dollar for services here. All you had to do was press the call button and someone would deliver the food for you."

I was stinging with resentment. So many years since our last vacation. It was partway between my husband's birthday and mine. Our Ashland trip had been our birthday gift to each other.

It took both Doug and me to help Dad stand up. We knew not

to pull on his arms; he was so fragile we could easily dislocate his shoulders. Instead, we put our arms around his torso and hoisted him to his feet.

Dad let out a loud groan. "Holy shit! What the hell are you doing to me?"

"We're taking you to the doctor so you won't have to make so much noise when you need to stand up," I said. After a five-minute struggle getting his jacket on, we were out the door.

"Get a move on, James M." Mom poked and prodded him, trying to get him to move faster as he shuffled down the long hallway, walker clomping, like he was running a fifty-yard dash.

"Can It get any uglier?" she whispered to me.

"Not now, Mom," I said. "This is not about you."

We were almost to the front door when she stared at Dad with disgust and said, "Egads, can he get any uglier? I can hardly stand It. And now we're living nose to nose in that tiny dump." She jerked her thumb back toward their apartment.

"You should never have left your San Jose house," I said.

"But we had that new house in Utah."

"That you couldn't wait to leave."

I looked at Doug. "This is such crap. She puts herself here, and now it's someone else's fault." I instantly felt guilty for violating my pledge that I'd behave myself when I was around her, that I could truly understand how sick she was, and to not hold her responsible. It was so much easier to promise than to do.

"Par for the course," Doug muttered as he hurried ahead of us to open the car door for Dad.

Dad was just a few weeks short of his ninety-third birthday. His swollen feet were like pontoons, neither stable nor flat enough for balance. He teetered to and fro, using his walker as a stabilizer. When he gained forward motion it took on a life of its own. He'd lean back to slow down, me scrambling behind him in case he fell, not sure how I would catch his two-hundred-pounds-plus weight. His feet stuffed in sheepskin slippers, he shuffled with impressive speed, teeth clenched, lips open, breathing through this mouth, working hard to keep going.

Mom chirped her discontent all the way to the front door, then stopped by the receptionist's desk to chat.

"Mom, we're leaving. You can go with us or stay here, but we're leaving."

She waved me away, then nodded in my direction. "Look who's in charge now," she said to the receptionist.

Doug slowly inched Dad into the car. He had to be turned around so he could sit down first, and then Doug lifted his legs in and pivoted him to face the dashboard. As his body rotated, the plastic bag covering the passenger seat crackled. A large bath towel muffled the sound, and neither Dad nor Mom appeared to notice. She had caught up with us at the car, having decided to join us after all.

"You sure have a nice car," Dad told Doug.

Doug gave me an eyebrow wiggle—Dad said that every time we took him anywhere.

"I'm going to buy one of these when we move back to California," Dad said.

We rode in complete silence for fifteen minutes before pulling up to the doctor's office. Getting Dad out of the car was even more difficult than getting him in; his pain appeared to be getting worse.

While Doug helped Dad, I asked the receptionist for a wheelchair. We checked in. And we waited. Nearly an hour passed before Dad's name was called. The doctor asked the nature of our visit, and I told her that Dad had fallen in the shower at his assisted living apartment.

"I mentioned that when I called for this appointment, and the facility also called and told you the same thing. They probably had more details than I do."

"He just fell," Mom said. "He falls all the time."

"Our X-ray technician has gone home," the doctor told us. "We have no way to diagnose his injuries. I'm afraid you'll have to take him to the emergency room at the hospital."

I couldn't believe what I was hearing. "When I arranged this appointment I was told, by this office and by the nurse at Dad's assisted living, that there was no emergency. And now you say we take him to the ER. You were told twice that there was a potential back injury involved—how could the X-ray tech just go home? We waited all day for this appointment. I could have taken him to the ER six hours ago. And he's been in pain all day!" I was furious with this doctor.

The doctor shrugged her shoulders. I looked at my husband, who was sitting quietly.

I tried once more with the doctor. "You have no idea how hard it is just to get him in and out of a car, and now that he's in pain, well…" I trailed off without finishing my sentence. Clearly, there was no help for us here.

I turned away from the doctor's complacent face. I kneeled next to the wheelchair. "Time to go, Dad. We need to take you over to the hospital."

We wheeled him as close to the car as possible and went through getting him situated again. He was now moaning with every move. Doug got behind the wheel and I sat in the backseat beside my mother. "I wish they would have told us something earlier," she said. "This has been a waste of my time."

Doug pulled up to the ER entrance. I asked an attendant for a wheelchair. By now I was cringing each time we asked Dad to move.

Doug wheeled Dad into the waiting room while I checked him in. The place was packed.

I asked the receptionist how long it would take for Dad to be seen. "If there are more serious injuries, we have to see those patients before we can see your father," she said. "What is the nature of your visit?"

"My parents live in an assisted living facility. They tell me Dad fell in the shower this morning, and he now has severe back pain. He also has stroke-related dementia, congestive heart failure, and Type 2 diabetes. He's had breathing problems all day."

I handed the assistant a list of Dad's medications.

"Does he have any allergies?"

"No."

I waited while she typed everything into the computer. She asked for his insurance information, and Mom reluctantly handed me her purse. She became frustrated when she couldn't immediately find her fan-folded credit card holder, which was kept together by a double wrapped rubber band.

"I'm his legal guardian," I told the receptionist.

She looked at me as though she didn't quite understand.

"I was appointed his legal guardian two months ago," I explained.

She made copies of Dad's insurance cards and handed them to me. I put them back in the card holder and gave Mom her purse. She immediately clamped it to her side under her arm.

I found Doug sitting with Dad in the waiting room, watching a wall-mounted TV. I excused myself and found a rest room. I dampened a paper towel and patted it over my face and neck. I thought about Doug sitting there in the pastel room; I knew how disappointed he was. Once again, our plans had been put on hold because of my parents' needs. I had reserved the tickets to the Ashland plays the previous December. Now it was May, and we were no-shows.

After an hour, Dad's name was called. We were directed to a small examination room.

"Where are we going?" Mom asked as we began to move Dad toward the room. Upon entering the ER, she had become quiet. These were the first words she had uttered since getting out of the car.

"Just down the hall so Dad can see a doctor," I told her.

Once Dad was situated, Doug left to go sit in the car.

Dad panted and groaned as he was moved from the wheelchair to the hospital bed. I helped the nurse pull off his shirt and pants and put on a hospital gown. He gasped and moaned as we tried to arrange him into a position that offered him some comfort.

Maneuvering Dad's two hundred and forty pounds was not an easy thing to do. Fortunately, his upper body and gripping strength were powerful enough to help steady him while we positioned him in the bed.

In the quiet of the ER exam room, Dad nodded off for a while. Mom occasionally indicated her unhappiness at having to wait so long. It was going on seven o'clock now. "What's taking so long?" she asked.

A doctor came in, and I told him why we were there. Mom offered nothing by way of explaining what had happened. I was hoping that she would at least confirm what I was saying. All I knew was what the facility staff had told me.

The doctor checked out Dad's reflexes. He looked at his eyes and ears and listened to his chest. He pulled him into an upright position and looked at his back, running his fingers along the spine. Dad was groaning. The doctor listened to Dad's chest again. He examined Dad's feet, and then came back to listen to the chest once more.

"Your father needs X-rays," the doctor said. "Someone will be here to take him to the lab."

Mom and I sat side by side crammed into a corner of the tiny exam room on orange plastic chairs never meant for the human form, our shoulders touching. Restless from sitting, I got up and paced the small space for a few minutes and then sat down again next to Mom.

"I got a letter from Uncle George," I said, breaking the silence. "He's doing well and sends his greetings to you." Mom said nothing.

I offered her a dog-eared copy of *People* magazine dated the previous year. She shook her head and turned away. She stared at her thumbnail and picked the cuticle.

Slouched in my chair I counted a total of sixty-three ceiling tiles. I was halfway through counting the floor tiles when Mom spoke.

"I pushed him," she said, staring at the blank wall behind the hospital bed.

"I pushed him," she repeated. "He made me so mad. I shoved him and he fell."

Forty-four

I n the quiet of the tiny exam room while Dad was away, Mom found her voice and fully unleashed it.

"I'm stuck wiping that old man's bum," she said bitterly. "I try to get him to the bathroom on time, but you see how he is, how slow. He shits his pants all the time."

She kept her eyes focused on the floor.

"This morning was a bad one. I can't tell you how bad it was. Shit was all down his legs. It smeared on the floor when I pulled off his pants. He can't do a damn thing for his self."

She picked at her thumbnail again.

"I was so mad. I told him to get in the shower."

She uncrossed her ankles and crossed them again.

"He was so slow in getting in the shower that I decided to help him a little. I pushed him. Then he fell."

I closed my eyes and kept quiet. I was stunned by what she'd admitted, and so thoroughly exhausted I couldn't think of a way to respond.

"I had to clean up his mess," she went on, "wipe his bum, and he needed a shower, so I pushed him. He moves so slow."

She fished in her purse for a nail file.

"He lost his balance and fell. You can't imagine what that bathroom smelled like, what it always smells like."

I opened my eyes. Again she uncrossed her ankles. Then crossed them. Then uncrossed them.

"He fell."

There was nothing I could say to her. Almost daily, I had told her to let the staff tend to Dad, and I had tried to convince her that if she did, she'd be relieved of the burden she so resented. The capable, experienced people who were willing and able to help Dad often told me Mom would stand at the door and refuse to let them in. They knew Dad needed them, and that he liked having them around. They were as frustrated as I was.

Mom and I sat once again in silence. At last, the X-ray technician wheeled Dad back in.

"The doctor has to review the X-rays," he said. "He'll be here soon."

Dad was drowsy, his eyes closed. Each breath was painfully drawn in and exhaled.

Within a half hour the doctor reappeared.

"Your father has signs of several old compression fractures that obviously went untreated," he said.

"Mom and Dad lived independently until two years ago. He used to fall a lot," I said. "He still falls a lot."

"I found no new fractures or sprains. But there is some fluid in his lungs." The doctor listened once again to Dad's chest. "He probably strained the muscles in his lower back when he fell."

"Dad has congestive heart failure," I explained. "He has a lot of swelling problems, especially in his feet and ankles. He's had pneumonia several times."

The doctor made some notes.

"We'll get him set up with a pain reliever, Darvocet, and send him home. If anything changes, bring him back here or take him to his regular doctor." With that, the doctor left.

A nurse came in with a Darvocet from the hospital pharmacy. She had Dad swallow it with a small cup of water. She handed me a piece of paper. "Here's a prescription that should cover him for the next week or so." She helped me get Dad dressed.

It was close to 8:30 by the time we stopped off at Rite Aid to get Dad's medicine. Doug offered to wait in the car with Dad while Mom and I went in.

"You sure have a nice car," Dad was saying to Doug as I closed the car door.

Inside the Rite Aid there was a secondhand store. "Oh, look," Mom said. "There are some purses over there." She headed straight toward them.

I followed her, talking to her back. "Mom, I'm going over to the pharmacy. I'll meet you back here."

There would be about a fifteen-minute wait for Dad's prescription. I went back to find Mom. She was holding two purses.

"Which one do you like? This one has a matching wallet."

"Mom, I don't really like either one of them. And you already have a ton of purses, some new ones that you've never used."

"Well, indulge me. Which one do you like?"

"Make your own decision. I'll get Dad's drugs. As soon as I get back here we're leaving. It's late, Mom, and Dad needs to get comfortable."

Back at the facility, I gave Dad's pain pills to the night attendant and then went to their apartment. Mom was standing at the open fridge in her kitchenette, reaching for the jug of Carlo Rossi wine.

"Mom," I said, "don't pour any for Dad. He's taking pain medication, and it won't mix with alcohol."

She waved me away. "Aaah, he always wants his wine, every night."

I wasn't too worried. Dad would probably fall asleep before he could chug his cheap wine. A staff attendant was there to help put him in bed. Mom was too busy wrestling her wine into a glass to notice that a caregiver was present so she made no complaints. Doug and I drove home.

With our Ashland plans trashed, the following morning we decided to go to an early Saturday matinee. On our way home we stopped by to see how Dad was doing. He was quite cheerful and surprisingly lucid.

"Hey," he said, getting up from his recliner, "you guys want a drink?"

Doug wrinkled his nose at the suggestion of drinking their cheap wine. "No thanks, Dad," I said. "We have a long drive home. Besides, you're on painkillers—you shouldn't be drinking at all."

"Your mother poured me a glass at lunch time and I'm fine," he said. He looked flushed and a bit too cheery, the way he always did after his first drink. His nasty moods after the first one never seemed to materialize anymore.

We chatted for a bit. I watched Dad as he sat back in his recliner. Doug gave me a thumbs-up as he, too, noticed Dad sitting with no sign of discomfort.

"I haven't seen your dad that chipper in years," he said as we walked to the car.

"Ah, yes, the wonders of modern pharmaceuticals and cheap wine."

On our way out the receptionist had shown me a note. It was on a torn piece of paper, half a sticky note, and it said that Mom and Dad were leaving. It was signed by both of my parents. Dad's signature could hardly be considered writing at all; it was just scratches.

"That looked like another thirty-day notice," Doug remarked as we drove.

"Yep, something to toss in the evidence file with the others, I guess."

We visited again the next day, Sunday, and again on Monday on our way home from work. Dad still seemed fine. I spoke with some of the staff members each time we visited. Dad was coming to the dining room for his meals, he was tolerating his pain medication quite well, and he was perky, talking to both staff and other residents.

One of the housekeepers said, "Your dad is so cute. He calls all of us 'dear' or 'darling' or 'sweetie pie.'" I smiled and told her we'd be back in a few days.

On my way out the door I asked the staff nurse how she thought he was doing. "He's having trouble coughing. That old congested chest of his needs a good cough from time to time. He's having trouble producing that deep, hacking cough that clears his chest. I'm sure he still has some pain, or he'd be coughing as hard as he usually does. Other than that, though, he seems fine."

That would be typical of Dad, not showing pain. Neither of my parents had ever let their vulnerability show—if they did, the other would see the opening to pounce and inflict more pain. I had only seen my mother cry once, after she pulled off a hangnail and her finger became infected. It swelled so badly that she had to go to the doctor and get it lanced. When she came home she locked herself in the bathroom and cried alone.

When I was a junior in high school, Mom and I went out shopping. When we got home Dad met us in the driveway. This was odd—he never came out to greet us or offered to help unload groceries when we came back from the store.

"Lila," Dad said. "Your mother called to tell you that your dad died." I knew Mom loved her parents, but she didn't shed a single tear upon hearing the news that her beloved father had passed. Any sign of weakness was like an open invitation for bullying and more verbal abuse. She got out of the car and went to her bedroom, closed the door, and spent the next hour on the phone. When she came out, there was an air of defeat about her, but she said nothing.

The Tuesday after Dad's fall we both worked late and headed straight home without seeing my parents. We had dinner and went to bed, taking a moment to share our profound disappointment that yet another vacation opportunity had slipped away.

"I guess it's a good thing that we hadn't left yet when the call about your dad came in," Doug said. "Maybe it was easier to give up the entire trip rather than get there and have to come home."

I nodded, glad that we could finally commiserate about our lost getaway, now that Dad seemed to be recovering.

Forty-five

Wednesday morning the phone rang just before our usual 4:30 wakeup time—that's how early we had to get going to put in our ten-hour workdays. It was the assisted living facility calling to let me know that the paramedics had taken Dad to the hospital. He was running a fever and having trouble breathing.

"Where's my mother? Is she at the hospital with Dad?"

"We just checked on her, and she went back to bed. She's sleeping right now. Do you want us to wake her up?"

"No. Let her sleep. I just wanted to know where she was."

Doug and I arrived at the emergency room around 5:30. The nurses were preparing to move my father to another room and put him on life support. I asked to see the ER doctor and found him reviewing Dad's chart.

"Your father has pneumonia," he said. "... I'm sorry to tell you, he's terminal." It was May 16. Dad was two weeks away from his ninety-third birthday.

He went on to explain that Dad was being moved to a room on the fourth floor and that the attending physician would explain more about his condition. When I found her I asked her about treating Dad's pneumonia—he had always beat it before.

"Even if we put him on an IV antibiotic, it wouldn't be enough to stop the infection. He would still be terminal. He could last a couple of days, or he could expire this morning."

I always carried copies of my parents' advance directives, my power of attorney, and my guardianship papers in my car; our house was too far away from town to go and fetch them during an emergency. Mom and Dad were both so old and fragile that I didn't want to be caught without such important information—I had known times like this would come around eventually. I had hoped that Dad would go to sleep one night and not wake up, go peacefully as his mother and his older brother had: no suffering, no decisions to make, just gone before waking. But I had to be prepared.

The time had come for me to speak on behalf of my dying father. He was semiconscious and in a lot of pain. The ER staff had just administered a dose of morphine and it was slowly taking effect. Dad barely knew who I was. I noticed he was still wearing his soiled pajamas, and that the cloth was thin and worn, almost frayed. I had bought him new ones, but Mom wouldn't let him wear them.

"When we get him settled on the fourth floor, he'll be on a morphine drip," the nurse told me. "The attending physician will order that very soon."

I had had pneumonia several times during my childhood, and I could attest to how painful it was. Dad no longer had the strength to cough deeply enough to help clear his lungs. He gasped and moaned as they moved him from the hospital bed to the gurney.

"Dad has an advance directive," I told the ER doctor. "He doesn't want any heroic measures to …"

He nodded. "Do you have a copy?"

I showed her my original with Dad's signature.

"Good. Good that you used one of our forms. It'll make it easier for us to find the information we need."

"Is this the right thing … the right time to do this?" I knew that neither of my parents wanted life support, feeding tubes, or anything that would prolong their lives if they should end up in a terminal state. All their directives asked for was comfort care.

"Yes," the doctor said. "This is exactly the right time to do this, before we hook him up to life support."

Now that the moment I had legally planned for had come, I felt awful. Taking responsibility for how my father would die weighed heavily. But this wasn't about me. Dad wanted to be let go, and I had promised I would see to it that he would be.

I walked alongside Dad's gurney as he was moved to the fourth floor. The morphine helped him relax—his eyes were closed, and he looked at ease. Every once in a while he raised his arm and reached out. I put his hand back on his chest and he seemed comforted.

Doug and I left the room so a nurse could insert a catheter, give him a sponge bath, put on a clean hospital gown, and change his diaper. "The doctor will be here soon," she told us before drawing the bed curtain closed.

While we waited I called Greg in California to let him know that Dad had pneumonia and had been diagnosed as terminal. I told him no one knew how long he would last.

"I'll call you later," I promised, "as soon as I have more information."

Then I called assisted living again. An aide told me that Mom was still in her room asleep.

Until that moment I had been in business mode: the responsible adult doing all the right things. But when I passed the news to this aide, someone at the facility with whom I had become friends, the reality of what was happening finally reached my heart. "Dad is dying. He won't be coming back today." I hung up the phone and burst into tears.

A hospital employee called a hospitalist told me that Medicare regulations would only let Dad stay for the night.

"Since your father has been diagnosed as terminal, if he's alive twenty-four hours from now, you'll have to move him to a nursing home."

I shook my head, not understanding what I was supposed to do.

The hospitalist tried again. "You'll have to make arrangements for your father to be transported to a nursing home if he's still alive by this time tomorrow."

I nodded, pretending to understand but still not grasping what I was being told.

"We will call two hospice providers. They will offer your father end-of-life care when he's moved to a nursing home. A representative from each hospice will be here so you can interview them and decide which one will be your father's caregiver. All hospice services are free of charge. While your father is here, the hospital staff will provide this care, but once he's moved, if he has to be, hospice will take over."

I went back to Dad's room and sat next to Doug. There was a small TV set, and Doug was surfing through the offerings. Dad raised his arm and reached out again as he had done before. I held his hand for a while. Then Dad tried to pull out the oxygen line.

"This isn't life support, in case you're concerned," a nurse told me as she inserted the tube back into his nostrils. "This actually makes his breathing a bit more comfortable. I'll also coat his lips with Vaseline to help soothe him. Let me know if there's anything else I can do."

Dad was on his side in a relaxed fetal position. His hand was on the move again. Sometimes it waved in the air, and sometimes it relaxed toward his nose and he pulled at the oxygen line. It would float toward his groin as he attempted to pull out the catheter. Each time I took his hand and tucked his arm back under the covers. It was warm, which seemed like a good sign, but the nurse had told us to watch his toes. The darkening purple in his toenails meant the pneumonia was starving him of oxygen.

At last my father's hand stopped its wandering. He slept quietly, clean, shiny, and free of distress.

Forty-six

By eleven o'clock that morning Doug and I were starving. The first hospice representative was due to arrive before eleven-thirty. We decided to wait for her and then get a bite to eat. Dad seemed stable.

When she arrived, she explained that her agency offered end-of-life care. All I had to do was sign on with them, and if Dad survived the night, I was to call them and tell them what nursing home Dad was in. They would care for him there.

She went into Dad's room, held his limp hand, and stroked his face. "He sure must have been a good-looking guy when he was younger," she said as she was leaving.

I marveled at the courage it must take to get up every morning and tend to the dying as this woman did. I thought about my own job as a technical writer, and the part that involved shadowing people in technical jobs and documenting what they did. I couldn't imagine writing a technical manual for hospice nurses. How could I document the instincts that guided them to do exactly what was needed at the moment, or how they prepared themselves to face another day filled with pain and distress?

When she was gone, Doug and I told the nursing staff we were leaving for lunch and to tour a couple of nursing homes. I called the director of Mom and Dad's assisted living facility and asked him which nursing home was good.

"Well, I'm not supposed to recommend anything," he said, "but I'd really stay away from that one on the west side and go for the one near the hospital. Go to both, though, so you can see for yourself and make up your own minds."

We started with the one he preferred. It was cheery, clean, and odorless. We were shown a room that was available for Dad, a bed he would occupy until he passed away. The hospice providers would tend to him, making sure that his pain medications were working and that he was clean and comfortable.

"Sometimes pneumonia patients can last several days or a week," the nursing care director told me. "Sometimes, this way of dying takes time."

On our way over to the next nursing home we drove through a fast food place and quickly choked down the food with a large soft drink. We both felt scummy. Neither of us had showered or brushed our teeth that morning, and now we were eating junk food.

Next we went to the other nursing home, and as soon as we entered the reception area we put our hands over our noses. The place reeked.

"I detect notes of urine and undertones of vomit along with a strong finish of shit," I said to Doug.

We waited for thirty minutes before anyone came out to greet us, breathing through our mouths and listening to the chaos beyond the lobby doors. We had decided to leave when a staff member, the admissions director, finally showed up.

I told our greeter about my dad's situation. She escorted us down a long hallway to an empty room at the end of the building. It was institutionally ugly with dirty windows, cracked floor tiles, stained ceiling tiles, and unkempt paint on the walls. I wanted out of there.

Down the hall we heard a man's voice wailing, "Help me. Help me. Help me."

"Do you need to attend to that person?" I asked.

"No," she said, "it's just what he does."

On our way out we walked past the howling gentleman. His wheelchair was too wide for the door frame. He kept backing up and, with a running start, ramming the wheels into the sides of the doorframe. "Help me. Help me. Help me."

"It's just what he does," I said to Doug, whose face was set in a grimace. We were positive we wouldn't bring a dying rat to this place. I called the first nursing home and told them I would contact them in the morning about Dad—if he survived the night.

Forty-seven

Our next stop was Mom's apartment. I had a brief conversation with the nurse and then the director. They knew that Dad was dying and would not return.

The director was one of the most wonderful men I had ever met. He sat with the residents during mealtime and listened to their stories. He served meals to the residents when the kitchen staff was super busy. He was the perfect guy for this kind of job. When I sobbed in front of him, he calmly handed me a tissue.

I was still sorting through our options. "Last year you mentioned that when Mom or Dad needed end-of-life care, they could stay in their apartment and the hospice nurses could care for them here. If Dad has to leave the hospital, would it be possible to bring him here?"

"Yes, we did make that offer," he responded. "And normally, it would be OK—other residents have received end-of-life care here. But your mother is mean, especially to your father. She has been quite cruel to him at times."

I nodded in agreement.

"So … we can no longer extend that offer. We would risk your mother attacking either your father or the hospice worker or another resident—someone frail—if she became aggressive. Watching a spouse die is rough business, and someone as dodgy as your mother could react in extreme ways. It's best if we don't go down that road."

I nodded my head in agreement, knowing full well that he was right. Mom was a loose cannon who could not be trusted at the best of times. Who knew what she would be capable of under these circumstances?

"I'm afraid the last person he needs at his bedside right now is his wife," he concluded. "I'm sorry."

I told him I understood, and that he was correct. I hadn't thought about Mom's aggression before inquiring about this option. Then I told him about Mom's confession at the ER. I thought he'd be surprised, but he already knew that she had caused Dad's fall.

He opened his mouth to speak, then hesitated. I could see him wrestling with something. Finally he said, "I feel I need to say this. Often after a person as frail as your father falls, they can't move about and keep fluids from pooling in their lungs. They die of pneumonia. It's quite common. That's why so many people who fall and break a hip never recover. In your dad's case, he injured his back, but it looks like the result is the same—death by pneumonia.

"One way to think about this, Karen, is that it's a kind of mercy. Pneumonia has been called 'the old man's friend' for hundreds of years. It's been considered the euthanasia of the elderly who are already dying. It simply hastens the process."

Forty-eight

Doug and I walked down the long hallway to Mom's apartment.

"So what's going on?" she asked.

"Mom," I said, "the news about Dad is not good. He has pneumonia. He's not going to make it."

Doug turned down the thermostat. It was hot in her apartment.

"Mom ... do you want to go to the hospital to say good-bye to Dad?"

"That bad, eh?"

I nodded.

She was quiet on the ride to the hospital and while we took the elevator to the fourth floor.

Mom stood before Dad's bed for several minutes. I pulled up a chair for her so she could sit beside him, then I turned to get one for myself to place next to hers. Doug had opted to stay outside in the hospital's park-like setting.

As I was grabbing the second chair, I heard Dad's bedsprings creaking. It was an unexpected sound, as if someone were bouncing on his bed. I turned just in time to see Mom raise her fist and slam it into Dad's shoulder. I watched in horror as she pummeled him again and again, making his body leap and the bed springs recoil. Too shocked to move, I watched as she hit him again, this time with both fists clasped together.

My feet were stuck to the floor as if caught on Velcro strips. I knew I should free myself to keep her from hitting him again, but I seemed to lack the strength or reflexes to separate my feet from the shiny tiles on the floor.

"Jim! *Jim!* It's me!" she yelled. "You *wake* up and you *look* at

239

me!" She drew back to slug him again. Still frozen in place, I could scarcely believe the power of the next punch.

It seemed like hours before I could move myself between them to protect my father. I could hear him moaning. "Mom," I said, searching for words to defuse the situation, "Dad is not feeling very well right now. Here, sit down."

"I want him to wake up and tell me who I am."

She refused to sit, instead scrambling to get past me. "Jim! You *wake up!*"

My thoughts were a crazy quilt, a chaotic jumble. I couldn't comprehend what Mom was doing to Dad. I had no idea what she wanted him to do, or say. I couldn't keep up with her, and I couldn't speak. I had watched them fight all my life, but there were no words for the horror of this: my mother was beating my father while he was on his deathbed.

Dad had been on morphine for hours to keep his suffering at bay. Somehow, through this drugged state, he slowly opened his eyes. My arms, which had been raised to protect him from Mom, dropped to my sides.

"Jim, you wake up, and you tell me who I am." Mom was seething.

Dad looked at her for a few minutes, his eyes never leaving her face. "You're my wife," he whispered, his voice shaking. He closed his eyes again.

They would be his last words.

Mom sat down. A nurse peeked in the door.

"Everything all right?"

I nodded dumbly, and she left.

Mom and I sat quietly. I looked at her and remembered watching her years earlier at their cemetery plot in California. As at that time, I had no idea what she might be thinking. And I was so aghast at what I had just witnessed, I was grateful for her silence; I didn't want to know what was taking place in her mind.

The only sound in the room was Dad's ragged breathing, like water chasing air through a garden hose.

Mom suddenly stood up. "Well," she said. "I am not accomplishing a damn thing here. I want to go home."

I called Doug on his cell phone, parroting her demand. "Mom

is not accomplishing anything here so she wants to go home."

"I didn't realize that she was in the middle of anything. I'll meet you at the entrance."

Back at assisted living, Mom fast-walked down the hallway to her apartment, obviously trying to escape us. She waved us away over her shoulder and went inside. I asked the staff to keep an eye on her and they told me they would.

Doug and I went back to the hospital. Dad's condition was unchanged. A representative from the second hospice agency we were considering arrived just past four in the afternoon. She and I went into a small break room next door to Dad's room. It was set up like a homey kitchen.

She pulled out a folder and put it on the table. She looked at me, ready to begin her orientation to their services, and I started to cry.

She reached across the table and gently took my hand. "You look like you've reached your information quota for today," she said, "so I won't stay." She pulled some items out of the folder. "Here's my card and our brochure. Please call me at any time if I can be of help."

She stood to leave. "You will get through this. We also offer grief counseling if you, your mother, or anyone in your family needs it." And then she was gone.

Doug came in to get a drink of water. "That was quick," he said.

"Yeah, it was. She was so kind and considerate—she could tell I'm on overload. She left us a brochure so we can look at it if Dad should need hospice. It all depends on whether he lasts the night …"

The director of Mom and Dad's assisted living facility came to the hospital to pay his respects to Dad. As we stood by Dad's bed, I told him about Mom's violent behavior. He nodded.

"You were so right," I said. "It's a good thing you didn't allow Dad to come back for his last few hours. Truly, there's no telling what Mom would have done to him if they were alone." I felt a little dizzy then, and I realized I was still reeling from having witnessed her assault.

By six that evening, Doug and I were hungry and in need of showers. We also needed respite, and our home was the only place we could find it. Maizie had been in doggy day care for most of the day, and it was time to pick her up and feed her as well.

"We're going to go home for a while," I told the nurse who was tending to Dad. "Do you think it will be all right to take a break?"

"Sure," she said, "but sometimes these cases can change quite rapidly. I have both your cell phone and home phone numbers. I'll call if things change."

We picked up our mail on the way up our long driveway. I called my brother, letting him know that Dad was still hanging on. While I was talking to Greg on our house phone, Doug's cell phone rang. It was the hospital.

"Your father's blood oxygen level is dropping. He's gone from ninety to fifty ... no, forty-five now. You'd better hurry." I knew that normal range was above ninety.

Within a half hour we were at the nurses' station. The one who had been taking care of Dad stepped out from behind the desk.

"I am so sorry," she said. "He passed about five minutes ago."

She led us to Dad's bedside. He was on his back with his hands folded across his chest, looking very peaceful, as though he were asleep. The catheter, morphine drip, and oxygen lines had already been removed.

We stayed with him for the next hour, just sitting quietly. I held his hand and patted his chest and kissed his forehead.

Doug and I agreed that there was nothing left to do at the hospital except call the funeral home. We got up to leave and stood together for a moment at the foot of Dad's bed, holding hands.

"'Bye, Dad," I said.

Mom and I had made arrangements with the funeral home a year earlier. They both wanted to be cremated. The idea appealed to Mom because she would have her very own space. Cemeteries were running out of available land; the one they had chosen in California would have had Mom and Dad stacked one on top of the other—whoever died last on top. Mom cringed at the idea of lying supine over Dad for all eternity, or worse, having him on top of her. Getting her funeral plans arranged had been very important to her, and now, in my exhausted state, I was grateful it had already been settled.

"We'll pick him up within the hour," the funeral director said. "I'm sorry for your loss."

We drove to assisted living, thinking we'd find Mom in her apartment, and were surprised to find her coming out of another resident's room. The minute she saw us, she raced away from us toward her own place.

"Is he dead yet?" she asked over her shoulder.

I hurried after her, forced to race-walk to catch up, my arms pumping and my arse jiggling from side to side. I was not about to yell back at her, "Yes, Mom, your husband is dead."

At her door we finally caught up with her. "Mom, Dad passed away. He's gone."

She waved us away.

"Mom, you can come to our house and spend the night if you want. Let's pack some things for you."

She pushed the door closed between us, making it clear we were not welcome in her space. "I give up," I said to Doug. "This day has been brutal enough. Let's go home."

On our way out I talked to the night aide and asked her to keep an eye on Mom.

"Of course. And I'm sorry for your loss, Karen," she said.

"Yeah, me too. Thanks."

On our long drive home I remembered that two months earlier the court had approved my guardianship petition for Dad. My intention had been to protect him from the predatory world that Mom wanted to drag him into. I wanted to shield him from her wild ideas, from one more harebrained move. How ironic that in the end I had not been able to protect him from the woman herself, from the relentless abusive force of his tiny one-hundred-pound wife.

My lawyer had told me that unless I was shackled hand and

foot to my parents, a guardianship order from the court couldn't really protect them. Now I knew he was right. Unless I had lived with them in their apartment and put myself between them, there was no way I could have prevented Mom's violent attacks on Dad. And even then, I knew my presence would have been no guarantee I could stop them. At the hospital that day, the suddenness of her aggression and the sheer shock of what I was witnessing had rendered me motionless; she had gotten in several harsh blows before I could even summon the presence of mind to command my own feet.

The next morning, I picked up Mom and we went to the funeral home. She chose a beautiful maple urn for Dad's ashes. I filled out one of her checks and paid the bill. The funeral director told us we could pick up the ashes in two days.

I took Mom to lunch. When we finished our meal I told her I was tired and that I had to make some phone calls. "You can come to our house if you'd like," I offered again.

She shook her head no, and I took her back to her apartment.

When I got home I called my brother and told him how peaceful and serene Dad had been at the end. It would be several weeks before I could tell him about the cause of his death and the beating he took from his wife on the day he died.

"Who would have thought that a man as violent as he was would go so quietly," Greg said.

Yes, I thought, in the end Dad did die peacefully, but the moments leading up to his death were as violent as the lifelong war Mom and Dad conducted against each other. There was no Versailles Treaty, no negotiation for an armistice. There was no forgiveness for past offenses.

My childhood prediction that one of them would kill the other had come true.

But I would tell Greg about this another day. For now, I told him about Mom's plans to move and what she'd lose if she moved and tried to live independently. "One never knows what she will do. Logic and reason have never applied to her," he said, summing up for both of us our lifelong experience as her children.

Mom and Dad wanted their ashes to be buried at the Ketchum

Cemetery in Idaho. When Mom passed, Greg, Doug, and I would take them there for the final good-bye. There would be no funeral, no ceremony. Dad didn't know anyone in Oregon, and Mom had refused to make friends with anyone here. Their friends were too old to travel. It was a relief that I had all these excuses to not plan a funeral.

I wrote a one-page eulogy for Dad and printed it on high-quality paper. I sent it out to their friends and family members to let them know of Dad's passing. Almost everyone had known that Dad's health was fragile; still, I made a few phone calls to select people so that when my letter showed up it wouldn't be too much of a shock. I also wrote his obituary for the local newspaper.

After the two-day wait, Mom and I went to the funeral home to pick up Dad's ashes. She looked haggard, whether from grief or guilt I could not know. It was possible that she had never linked Dad's fall with his death or realized that she had any part in it. To this day, I have never talked to her about it or asked her how much she remembers. There would be no point; even if she felt like communicating—a rare occurrence now—it is not in her character to accept responsibility for anything.

After picking up Dad's ashes Mom and I went to lunch, leaving him on the back seat of my car. The maple urn was beautiful, like a finely crafted piece of furniture. Mom told me that she wanted to keep it in her apartment.

When I took her back to her place, she put the urn on Dad's recliner. "That way I can still yell at him," she said, her eyes flitting to me briefly. She turned away, shoulders slumped, and I thought that she might finally grieve. Then she straightened and looked at me again.

"Are you my guardian?"

"No, Mom, but I'm still trying."

I had no idea why the question was important to her now.

On one of her many shopping trips, Mom had bought a set of stickers, the ones that have hearts and stars and a few words on them, the kind you would put on a letter or a card and mail to someone. She rummaged in a drawer and pulled out a sheet of them along with a pen.

I watched as Mom put one of these stickers on Dad's fine maple urn. It said, "Missing You." In a small blank space, in blue ink, she had written: Jim, May 16, 2007.

Forty-nine

Several days after Dad died I got a phone call from assisted living. It was the director.

"Hey Karen," he said. "We have a bit of a problem with your mother. She's barging into other residents' apartments and trying to give away all of your dad's things. She just opens doors and tosses in your dad's stuff—slippers, electric razors, T-shirts. She seems convinced she has the right to do this, but people are getting upset. Some of these things haven't been washed. I've gone around and collected everything I know about. They're in a box in my office. Can you come and get them?"

I drove there and picked up the box and put it in my car; there was no point in returning anything to Mom's apartment. Then I walked down the long hallway to her room.

Her place was devastated. I would have thought she'd been vandalized—if vandals could be attracted to a trash heap.

"Hey, Mom, what's going on?"

"No point in keeping any of this junk," she said. She was pulling more of Dad's things out of drawers and closets and tossing them on the floor. She stopped and held up an item, glancing my way. "I think I'll keep this, his leather jacket."

Her voice cracked and her eyes got watery—I was sure she would let herself grieve for a moment. But instead she turned back and continued pitching Dad's things onto the floor.

"Mom, you don't have to do this now. If you wait until this weekend, Doug and I will help you."

"Oh no, I'm not waiting for anyone. I'm moving. I've been talking to my friend in California and she's finding real estate agents for me. I'm moving back to San Jose and buying a house. I won't see you again after I move. You know that."

I sighed and turned away from the sight of my mother generating further chaos. Countless times I had wished for parents who could help me learn how to live my life. Lacking such support, I had stumbled and fallen many times before figuring things out for myself. *Parents give us life,* I mused, not for the first time, *but they're not always around to help us live it.* Sometimes that's left up to us, and we have to look forward, not behind. If we drag our feet in the dust of the past, it clogs our minds, obscures our vision, and makes it impossible to take in a good lungful of fresh air.

Standing there in my mother's assisted living apartment, I truly wanted the ability to draw in a deep, cleansing breath. And I wanted to know what I should do; I wanted a wise mommy and a wise daddy to guide me. I had only myself to rely on. My hands started to shake, and I wanted my inhaler.

"So Mom, if you don't mind my asking, what are your plans? I mean, since I'm not your guardian and you can go anywhere."

For the first time since I had arrived, she looked straight at me as if to try to size me up. I could almost hear her thoughts: Was this a trick question? Was I trying to pump her for information that I could eventually use against her?

"My friend is finding a motel for me on Stevens Creek Boulevard where I'll stay until I can find a house. I'll put all of my things in storage for a while."

"But Mom, you'll lose two thousand dollars a month in long-term care benefits. You'll have no access to your medications."

"You are not my guardian, so butt out."

I tried a different tactic. Instead of telling her what she couldn't do, I decided to act as her confidant. She loved to tell people how clever she was—I'd play along. I would no longer mention things like the fact that I was the appointed caregiver in her advance directive, or trustee of her estate. When I was through here, I would head straight to my lawyer's office and beg him to fast-track my petition for full custody of her, before she got lost in the world. But for now, I would involve myself in her plans.

"You know, Mom, even though I oppose your plan to leave this safe environment, the least I can do is help make sure your plans include personal safety and comfort. You're a single woman now, so don't do anything foolish."

All I got in response was her curled lip.

Fifty

Two weeks after Dad died I saw another attorney, one who specialized in elder law. I was searching for a second opinion as to whether I should continue my battle to get custody of Mom. I explained to him how long it was taking, how much money Mom was blowing, how dangerous she was, and how much it was costing us, among other details.

"OK," he said. "None of what I have to say is going to be easy to hear. First, you need to get your mother chipped," he said.

"Chipped? Like my dog is chipped?"

"Pretty much. Unfortunately, morgues don't have the ability to scan bodies for ID chips, so you might want to have her tattooed instead, or put a bracelet on her—one that can't be removed."

I sat with my mouth open, shredding a Kleenex into molecular dust in my lap.

"Does it seem like a big leap from her moving away to her landing in the morgue? It's not. Here's what's likely to happen to your mother if she escapes, especially if she goes to a big city as she seems to be planning and especially if she moves to a motel. First, she will get lost. And immediately after that, she will be preyed upon. There are creeps everywhere just looking for a tiny, frail woman like your mother. Her predators will be helpful to her to gain her trust. Her social security number will be stolen, along with her Oregon ID and any credit card and bank account information. They will ask her to sign a new power of attorney. Once that's done all of her assets will be gone. Then she could simply disappear. The statistics on missing John and Jane Does in urban areas are staggering. If her body is ever found and not identified, she will be cremated and her ashes will go in a common burial plot. You'll never find her."

I sipped some water and reached for a second Kleenex.

"You'll have to file a missing persons report. If they find some-one they think might be her, you'll be asked to fly somewhere to try to identify her—or whatever is left of her. You've told me she has no teeth, so dental records won't help. And if she's decom-posed beyond recognition … well, let me just say that you could spend the rest of your life looking for her."

By the time I got to the car I was sobbing. Doug drove, and I sobbed all the way home.

"It's too much, way too much," I cried. "We've done every-thing for her. We've given up our lives for her, our vacations, our money, our time. And now to be told that we may spend the rest of our lives searching for her if she disappears. It's just so over-whelming."

I blew my nose.

"And Mom, she's so tiny and frail, and her brittle bones. One good conk on the head and she's toast. She's so full of energy and righteousness for now. Can you imagine her fear, her terror if she were accosted by some criminal?"

I hiccupped and blew my nose again.

"And she still has access to all of her money. I think it's around six hundred thousand dollars. Even if she survives, after she's robbed of everything … It's just like my lawyer told me. Now that Dad has died, I have no hold on her at all. I can't use my guard-ianship of him to anchor her anymore. I don't know what to do, Doug, I really don't."

My husband had no answers for me.

A few days later I visited Mom again. She was lighthearted and chipper—way too lighthearted and chipper, like a teenager on the eve of a prom night with the big man on campus. She was playing music on her new radio, one of the many she had ordered recently. She now had five CD player/radio sets and dozens of clocks, all still in their boxes.

The radio was tuned to a hip-hop channel, and it was a little loud, but it didn't seem to bother her at all. Her cheeriness set the intuitive voices howling in my head. She was up to something, and if it made her this happy, no good could come to it. *She thinks she's getting away with something.*

When I dropped in a couple of days later, she was distraught. She fluttered a bill from an ambulance service in my face.

"They're charging me almost nine hundred dollars to take your father to the hospital. You and Doug took him! I went with you, so I know he didn't ride in any ambulance."

I looked at the bill. Sure enough, nine hundred dollars.

"And I want you to write a letter to the head corporation of this place," she went on. "Someone put medical equipment in my room. I am not a storage unit!"

"Mom," I said. "Yes, Doug and I took Dad, and you too, to the doctors' office and then to the hospital the day he fell. But five days later he got sick and the paramedics came to get him. This bill is legitimate, and you don't have to worry, your insurance will pay for most of it. And yes, the facility left a wheelchair and an oxygen tank when they were here, but they came back and got it the next day. It has nothing to do with this bill."

"I didn't order any of that. And it was you and Doug who took your father to the hospital. I am not paying this!"

Her body was tensing up, her shoulders bunching up around her ears and her fists clenched. This was a woman who never even spanked me or my brother; she was certainly verbally abusive, but never physically. Now she looked as if she wanted to punch someone. Her face was a grimace.

I quickly turned to the window, looking out at the open meadows that surrounded the facility. It was time to put to use what I had learned in my Alzheimer's support group: that when my mother stopped making sense or got upset it was best to change the subject immediately.

"Look, Mom," I said. "There's a killdeer—you know, that bird that pretends to be wounded to draw attention away from her young."

She came over to the window and looked out. "I don't see a damn thing."

"Would you like me to wash your dishes for you?"

"No, the housekeepers keep this place clean."

I looked around. The room was, by Mom's definition, clean. Clutter and heaps of junk covered up most of the dirt. The smell from the kitchen sink told me that there was food rotting there.

"So, what are your plans?" The change of subject had worked; she had calmed down considerably.

"I'm leaving this place, and you can't stop me."

She fiddled with a TV remote control, shaking it and pushing the buttons. "I want to turn that music off."

"Can I see that? Maybe I can fix it for you."

She handed it to me and I could tell by the weight of it that it didn't have batteries installed. After some digging, I found the remote for the radio and turned it off.

"Hey, you're not my guardian, are you?" she asked.

"That's right, Mom. I'm not your guardian. I'm still trying, but no success yet. I was Dad's guardian but that ended with his death."

I spotted several brochures for motels in the San Jose area sticking out of an envelope. The return address on it was from her friend in California. So this much was true—she had someone helping her. I also saw a moving estimate from Bekins; she had a collection of those that could fill a book.

"So, it looks like you're going to travel," I said, keeping my voice light and casual. "Tell me about your plans." My hands were sweating. At any moment she could clam up and I'd never find out. I tried my best to appear excited for her so she would share more.

She told me her friend had decided it would be best if Mom took a train to San Francisco. Mom hated flying; it bothered her ears. A taxi would take her from assisted living to the Amtrak station in Albany. After arriving in San Francisco, she would take a commuter train down the peninsula to San Jose. Her friend would meet her there and drop Mom off at the motel. Her belongings would be stored at the huge Bekins warehouse in Gilroy, quite a distance from San Jose. Mom would live in the motel until she found a house to buy.

"Well, Mom, that sounds like a plan. I think you're missing a few things though. Like your medications. I can call your doctors and make appointments—"

"No," she interrupted me. "I have no reason to see them ever again."

"Well, they could help you, actually. You could get your prescriptions, the paper kind, and have them filled at a pharmacy in San Jose. And then you would once again have control over your pills. No more med aide treating you like a two-year-old waiting for you to swallow. Wouldn't you like that?"

The idea really appealed to her, so I called her doctors and made appointments. Then I wrote them brief letters, describing how Dad had died, the nightmare of her attacking him on his deathbed, and the fact that she was now so manic that she couldn't see straight. I also pointed out that if she left, she would have no access to her medications and she would lose a huge chunk of her monthly income. I added that Mom had spent almost all the money in her checking account.

Two days earlier, I had palmed one of Mom's bank statements into my purse when she was in the bathroom. I also grabbed a fist-ful of documents from huge stacks of neglected paperwork, notic-ing when I did so the business card of the representative from Bekins. He was someone I had talked to many times, and I knew he was helping me protect Mom by using tried-and-true delaying tactics.

The paperwork I had grabbed was too big for my purse. I opened the hallway door and set the pile outside, shoving it in a plastic grocery bag. Once I said good-bye to Mom, I could retrieve it on my way out.

When Mom returned from the bathroom I asked, "Hey, Mom, have you called Greg or Kristen to let them know that you're re-turning to the Bay? They could meet your train."

"No." She said with nothing further to say.

"Where does your friend live?"

"In Saratoga, not too far from the country club."

There was no bus service to that part of the Bay Area. And if Mom tried to hail a taxi in San Jose or San Francisco (assuming she ever made it that far), surely someone could fool her into believ-ing that they were there to help her. I could easily imagine her meeting someone on the train, pouring her heart out, and becom-ing the victim of a scam—or worse—either during her trip to the Bay Area or as soon as she got there.

I probed enough to discover that she had no plans for anyone to meet her, not even her best and oldest friend who still lived near Mom's old San Jose house. Mom would try to navigate the entire trip by herself.

If she couldn't find her way to the big front door of her dentist's office, how could I believe she could plan this trip and make it there alive?

Fifty-one

Mom believed me when I suggested that one last visit to her physicians would be a good idea, solely for the purpose of picking up prescriptions she could take to a pharmacy somewhere in the Bay Area; the idea of having control over how and when she took her meds had taken root. Right in front of her, Mom's primary care physician and I talked about moving her to a memory-loss facility. We both looked at her to see if our conversation was registering. She was so deeply into the world of her new plan that she had tuned us out completely.

The doctor wasted no time. "I can sign the paperwork to move her immediately," he said.

"But her lawyer still insists that she's completely normal and capable. Let me talk to my lawyer and see if my petition is progressing."

I have always regretted not jumping on this offer to move Mom to a memory-loss facility right away, but I was positive that her lawyer would interfere. I wanted to have full legal approval from the court to be her caregiver first. Her lawyer's threats to have me arrested for all those bogus charges caused me to hesitate. I balked and asked her doctor to delay until I had secured legal consent.

I could imagine Mom's attorney securing a court order to have her released from a memory-care facility, and if that happened, the only place Mom could go was the street. I thought it was better for her to stay where she was while I worked with the legal world to make sure her lawyer could not intervene. If he were to find out that her doctor and I were considering moving Mom to a memory-loss facility, he would never agree to anything contained in my petition.

"Well, OK—call me as soon as you hear. She needs to be protected from herself."

Our next visit was to the neurologist's office. She proposed that Mom give this move back to California a trial run. I was a bit shocked that her doctor would suggest this. It's the last thing that I wanted: Mom out there in public and alone.

"Lila, you shouldn't do anything suddenly right now, so soon after your husband has passed away. Plan a short trip to your friend's home, and look at houses with that as a base rather than move into a motel. Living alone would be dangerous for you, especially with no car. How will you get around? So try that first. Then as soon as you get back here you can finalize your moving plans."

The neurologist looked at me then. "You can't help her. As I've been telling you all along, she has to either succeed, which is doubtful, or fail all on her own. It's just like your lawyer says—if she fails her lawyer will have no doubt and no case. If she can't put together a simple plan for a short trip to California, in addition to all of the other evidence, no judge in the world will deny your petition for her custody."

"But there is a huge danger for her, even on a short trip," I said. "Should we even encourage her to go anywhere on her own?"

"She'll be tested by the challenge to plan a trip, and it might help deter her from planning something larger, like a big move out of state. If she can't manage even a quick trip, it will be one more thing to present to the court."

Mom was still oblivious to our conversation, lost in what was left of her brain, making plans for her perfect life, the life she had always dreamed about. This time Mom scored a fifteen on the MMSE test. She couldn't repeat back simple phrases like "no ifs, ands, or buts." She couldn't recall three simple words such as tree, ball, and cat just three minutes after these words were given to her. She couldn't replicate a simple drawing of a triangle, tell the doctor what building she was in, or name the date.

Mom did score high on personal information such as her birth date and where she was born. But she couldn't extend her arms and bring her forefingers to her nose with her eyes closed, and she couldn't balance on one foot. And she no longer walked heel-to-toe—she shuffled.

The doctor made some notes, then turned to me and said, "Your mother has frontal variant fronotemporal dementia, or fvFTD. One of its symptoms, emotional blunting, can also be seen in her lack of facial expression and her inability to grieve for your dad. Also, her loss of insight, that she cannot be introspective, and that she has difficulty planning and carrying out those plans all point to FTD. It may seem like she's busy trying to make a new life for herself now, but all her plans will end in failure or she will try to make plans that are doomed to fail.

"Your mother has signs of Parkinson's disease," the neurologist added. "That's what the shuffling is about. It could be Parkinsonism caused by her antipsychotics—hard to tell. If you live long enough, Parkinson's will come along. But she also has what we call 'flat affect.' I'm sure you've noticed that her expression is neutral. She's mostly devoid of any expression at all."

I looked up flat affect on the web when I got home that day; it was associated with schizophrenia. Did I need any more evidence that Mom should be in protective custody?

Fifty-two

The next day I went to my lawyer's office. "I was just about to call you," he said.

He handed me a piece of paper. It was from Mom's attorney.

"The judge sent notice to your mother's attorney. He's a bit peeved that this case has been on his docket since last fall. He wants us to get busy, so now her attorney wants to set up a meeting—you, me, him, and your mother."

"Wow, sure, I'm happy to meet with the two of you, get things moving. I have to insist, though, that Mom cannot attend this meeting. If she gets unstable the whole thing could be a waste of time. She's been really manic lately."

"OK then. Let's see where this gets us. And Karen, by the way, did you happen to tell your mother that she was free to move anywhere she wanted?"

"Last week she asked me again if I was her guardian. I told her no, but that my petition was still active in the legal system. She sees this as a green light. Her neurologist told her to plan a short trip to California, knowing that Mom is incapable."

"Well, for some reason she thinks that this whole thing is over with. Her attorney does think that she needs someone to oversee her finances, but she doesn't want you to be the one. She doesn't want you to have any control over her."

"Yeah, I know. I'm A-B-B-Y, any-body-but-you, but this is old news. So how will this meeting work?"

He gave me a list of everything I needed to bring with me. I had to supply, once again, a list of Mom's assets, their account numbers, and the names and addresses of each institution. I went home to my spreadsheet. There were pieces missing since her lawyer had insisted that I butt out of her money management, so it wasn't completely accurate, but it was as complete as I could make it.

"You also need to bring your mother's watch back," my attorney said.

"What?"

"Your mother has accused your husband of stealing her sister's watch. Her lawyer said that this was a deal breaker. No watch, no deal."

I told him about being in my car with Mom and how she had held up her late sister's wristwatch and asked if Doug would fix it. "The last time I saw that watch was when Mom was dropping it back into her purse.

"My aunt and uncle led modest lives. That watch could not have been valuable, and whether it is or not, we don't have it. She wanted Doug to take out a link so she could wear it, but she never gave it to us. Doug has never seen that watch."

He scribbled a few things on a yellow legal pad.

"Besides," I continued, "if that jerk ever brings up this missing watch, I would like to remind him of all the money Mom has lost since she's been under his 'protection.' I'm sure that the Oregon Bar Association would love to hear about that. Tell that guy that he's wrong and has never been more wrong. If he wants my mother's watch, then he can go and find it. I would love to see his face after he's plowed through all the garbage and filth in her apartment. He's been there several times—surely he's seen the chaos."

There would be no mention of the watch again until much later. And the accusation that I was stealing my mother's assets disappeared forever. It just fell off the edge of the earth along with her lawyer's promise to share the results from the second-opinion tests.

I told Mom about the meeting and she seemed relieved to get it over with so she could be on her way. Then I deliberately lied, using her infirmity against her: I knew she was uncomfortable being around more than one person. I had no qualms about the deception.

"Mom, you know that other people will be there. My lawyer, your lawyer, Doug, me, Greg might come up, a notary, and a secretary. We'll be together in a conference room at my lawyer's office."

Mom fidgeted a bit. "I prefer to not be there."

"Well ... OK. I'll tell my lawyer you won't be there."

I didn't say anything to her about a possible reason she was uncomfortable around others: that she wore the same food-stained clothing day after day. I didn't know if this was because she had so much junk piled in front of her dressers and in her closets that she couldn't reach her clean clothes. Or perhaps her hesitation had nothing to do with this and she was unaware of how she looked. She had her hair washed, set, and combed weekly and got a perm and a cut about every three months, all done by a lovely woman at the facility. In between, she rarely combed her hair, instead walking around with "bed head." I combed her hair for her when we went out, but when she stayed in she looked grimy and unkempt. She never let any of the aides tend to her hygiene. They were scared of her anyway, so they did as she said and left her alone.

She was afraid of falling, so she avoided the shower and tried to keep clean with just a washcloth at the sink. The registered nurse who had taken care of Dad's feet and nails had started taking care of Mom's hands and feet as well. Before that, her nails had grown into claws, dirty and snagged. Why it was OK to have people attend to her hair, hands, and feet but not help her bathe was beyond me, but Mom avoided any situation that involved intimacy.

Each time I saw her and took inventory of her declining state, I feared more and more the thought of her living alone in a world that was not kind to the elderly or the feeble. I knew that every community is fraught with crimes against old people. I was determined that Mom would not be abused by anyone. The irony was that she was convinced that I was her sole abuser.

Considering my history with her, I should have just kept my distance and left her to her own devices. Doug and Greg and I talked about that possibility several times: just let her go. Turn the responsibility for her life back over to her. But she was tiny and old and frail. And she was plagued with this horrible disease that had turned her once-functioning brain into a cruel joke, betraying her at every opportunity. Conflicted as I was, and as painful as it was to suffer her hostility, I couldn't bring myself to let her try and fail to fend for herself.

Mom had lucid moments, and she was good at fooling people for a while. I found sticky notes all over her apartment that were basically flash cards—a sign that she knew what she had lost and was doing what she could to get it back.

Scratch the surface, though, and the truth was there for anyone to see. Written on her handmade flash cards were dozens of lists of medications. She had gotten low marks from her doctors because she couldn't tell them the drugs' names, dosages, or purposes, or the warnings that came with them. Mom had become a person who couldn't see the filth around her, manage her money, or realize that she needed help with basic hygiene, but she was obsessed with memorizing her medication list, thinking that reciting her med list verbatim was the way to gain her freedom.

I was eager for the upcoming meeting of the attorneys, yet anxious about what the results would be. These two men would lay the groundwork for Mom's future.

Fifty-three

A couple of hours before the meeting, Doug and I met with my lawyer in his office. He leaned back in his office chair, gazed at the ceiling for a minute, and then looked at us. "OK, so here's the deal." I squirmed in my chair.

"Your mother's lawyer has offered conservatorship only, no guardianship. So you will have to drop your petition for guardianship. In addition, your mother insists that your brother is the only one who can be her conservator. If we do not accept this offer, we'll have to go to court to pursue guardianship, and if your mother is not the drooling village idiot at that moment, the judge may see her as competent. Her lawyer will speak for her, so she may never have to say a word. Also, as I've mentioned before, we won't be able to introduce your mother's medical records. She's protected from that exposure, so the court may never see how many medications she takes or how much Alzheimer's has damaged her. Those MMSE scores will be hidden from the court."

He played with his tie for a while.

"Also, if you try to persuade the judge by telling him how your father died, well, that's just hearsay, something you could have made up, so it's not wise to try to play that hand. There were no witnesses and there is no police report. Your mother wasn't arrested for injuring your father. All anyone knows is that an old man fell down and was injured, and that those injuries led to his death."

The three of us sat there. I slumped forward in my seat as my hopes of coming to a settlement that would protect my mother fell to dust around my feet.

Doug took out his Swiss army knife and poked at his fingernails with the metal file.

"So a conservatorship is control over the money," he said.

"Control over every penny?"

"Yes, each and every cent," my lawyer replied.

"And guardianship is control over the person but not the money? Making medical and housing decisions and such, but no money?"

"Yes."

"And Karen would retain her power of attorney, her POA, which already gives her the power to make medical and housing decisions for her mother, right?"

"That is correct. As far as we know, Karen's POA has not been revoked—there's no record at the courthouse of a revocation ever being filed. There's only the original notarized paperwork stating that Karen has her mother's POA."

"OK." I could see Doug's wheels turning. "Now, if Greg controls Lila's money, he pretty much controls Lila, right?"

I sat up.

"If Greg is her conservator," my husband went on, "he won't let her pay for a taxi ride, or buy an Amtrak ticket, or pay for a moving van service, or a motel room—or a lawyer for that matter."

"He would have that kind of control, yes," my lawyer confirmed.

It took some time to sink in, but eventually this seemed like the very best plan for Mom: separate her from her money and she couldn't use it to bring about her own destruction. There was hope here after all.

My lawyer turned to me. "Karen, as conservator your brother would make all of the monetary decisions for Lila, down to every cent. He would have to file a financial report with the court each year. The judge isn't asking for a bond to protect your mother's assets, nor is her attorney, so that annual report is all that will be required. We can file it from this office, as it will have to go through a legal review first."

A few minutes later Mom's lawyer came into the office and we met briefly. I had never seen him before, and he reminded me of Dan Quayle, with that blank, deer-in-the-headlights look of someone who lacks a finely tuned brain. I had researched him online and found one complaint against him. It had been resolved, so we hadn't been able to disqualify him to handle Mom's affairs. This didn't stop me, though, from qualifying him as a moron. Only incompetence could account for his willful disregard for my mother's circumstances.

We were coming up on Fourth of July week, and we knew that both attorneys and the judge would be out of town soon. We could only hope that the judge would issue the letters of conservatorship before the holiday began. Then, at last, all of Mom's impossible plans would be legally halted once and for all. And her lawyer would be in the past, where he belonged.

I was so relieved, so happy, so encouraged. We had finally found a way to create a future that would not hold the fear of Mom being robbed, raped, buried in a shallow grave, or tucked into the trunk of a car and lost forever.

Fifty-four

Juty 4, 2007, fell on a Wednesday. Doug and I would be taking Thursday and Friday off, and we worked long hours Monday and Tuesday to complete our projects so we wouldn't have to return to work until the following Monday. Tuesday evening we met friends for dinner. Doug and I were looking forward to some relaxation. The legal wheels had slowed again, and we had resigned ourselves to the fact that the conservatorship would not be resolved until after the Fourth of July holiday week was over.

We were sitting on a patio, ordering our dinner, when I heard my cell phone ringing. The restaurant was on a busy street, and I could barely hear my caller. It was the receptionist from Mom's assisted living facility.

"Karen, your Mom is moving out the day after tomorrow. She's given us a written notice. She's been bragging about this move to the housekeeping staff. The only detail I have is that the moving company is somewhere down by Eugene. I think it's Bekins—or some local company that works for Bekins. It's not the people you've been working with. She told me that the court said that you are no longer her jailer and she can now do anything she wants."

Fear thudded in my stomach.

"Karen," Doug said, "what's wrong?"

Back home I looked up every moving company in the Yellow Pages as well as online. There was one moving and transfer company just north of Eugene that had a Bekins logo in its ad, an independent company that used Bekins for storage services. I called them that evening and all through the day of the Fourth, but it was obvious they were closed for the holiday.

Early on the fifth, after a sleepless night, I called again.

"Hi," I said. "My name is Karen Peck and I'm the daughter

of Lila McRoberts. I understand that she's planning a move to California."

"Yes, we have a crew together and we'll be there to load up the truck in about three hours."

"She cannot move," I blurted out. "I have her power of attorney, and a judge is about to sign conservatorship over to my brother. He will have full control of her money, and he is not going to pay you."

The receptionist put the sales rep who had made the arrangements on the phone. "Lady, we've got time invested in this move."

"I understand, but please listen. My mother has Alzheimer's disease. My father died recently, and she's been crazy since he passed away. Her doctor is about to sign an order for her to be put into a memory-care facility." I was lying—again—without a single pang of regret. After all, what was wrong with this man? He had seen firsthand how old and frail she was and where she was living, and he never questioned that?

"I have no idea who you are," he said. "You could be anyone, anyone at all, interfering with this woman's life."

"Yes, that's right, I can be anyone, and so can you. But if your truck pulls up to my mother's assisted living facility, the staff will call the Corvallis police and we'll go from there. Then you and I can meet at my attorney's office and sort things out."

"Now don't go getting all—"

"I am sorry for this inconvenience, and I am more than willing to pay you for the work you've done so far. Please send me an invoice and it will be paid promptly. But please understand, this woman is my mother and she does have Alzheimer's."

"Well, OK ... I'll have to let your mother know that you cancelled her plans, though. I'm sure that she will be very unhappy."

"Yes, fine. Tell her what you need to tell her," I said. "It's been a long time since someone told my mommy on me."

The next day our phone rang and rang and rang. Caller ID said that it was Mom. She left one message after another.

"It's *me*. It is *I*."

"My plans!"

"You, you, *you* call me!"

And on and on this went, way into the evening hours. Doug

turned off the volume and erased all of her messages. There was no way I could reach my lawyer. He was out of town until the following week. And I wasn't about to go see my mother. The staff at assisted living gave me updates each time I called to check on her.

My biggest fear was that she would call her lawyer and bring all of our progress to a screeching halt. She could easily change her mind about agreeing to the conservatorship deal. She could be calling her lawyer with the same frequency as she was calling me. He was out of town too, but he'd be back, probably before the judge signed off on putting Greg in charge of all her money.

Assisted living called again. "Your mother has had two taxi-cabs here today. One way or another, she is determined to leave. She went outside and walked down the street, and she was out there for about half an hour. One of our staff members was leaving to go home and saw her. She picked up your mom, and she told her she had been waiting for a bus. We have no bus service here, or even close, as you know. She was quite upset to be brought back here and she swears that she'll leave by any means possible."

Not knowing what else to do, I called the ombudsman at the facility, the man assigned to protect residents. He had been kept apprised of Mom's actions.

His advice was to go to the police department and see if they could connect me to the district attorney's office. His hope was that I could get a restraining order, which would force Mom to stay at the assisted living facility until the letters of conservatorship could be signed and issued.

Next I called the manager of the facility and asked if they could enforce such a restraining order.

"I am so sorry, Karen, but we can't. I am very aware of your mother's situation, and we will help in any way that we can, but all assisted living facilities are at-will places. Any resident can come and go as they please. We cannot restrain your mother, and no judge can enforce an order like that. She is still a person who has rights, freedom to move about."

I called the ombudsman back, and once again he suggested that we visit the police department—for what I wasn't sure, but we went anyway. An officer escorted us into a room where we could talk. I told him the whole story, beginning from the time

Mom and Dad sold their San Jose house and moved to Utah.

He cursed Mom's lawyer. "How in the hell can anyone help a woman in your mother's condition try to live alone?" I could see his muscles bulging underneath his Kevlar vest—I would hate to be on the receiving end of this man's ire.

"Look," he said, "there are no laws on the books that will protect your mother. If she wants to move, legally, she can go anywhere. But I do understand that she's not competent and that she'll be a target for any predator, or she could get lost or fall off a bridge or get hit by a train. I get that." He sat back and thought a while.

He leaned forward. "So, here's what you do."

Both Doug and I gave the officer our full attention. This was a make-or-break time in the care of my mother.

"After you leave here, go to that assisted living place and tell them, and put it in writing, that if anyone comes to get your mother they are to make a 911 call immediately. An officer will respond, and he will give your mother a brief field test to see if she is competent, you know, ask her some questions about her plans. Chances are she'll fall apart under the pressure and give the officer a reason to take her to the hospital, the psych ward, for an evaluation."

I cringed at the thought of Mom being put in a police car and taken to the hospital.

"They'll only be able to hold her for seventy-two hours, though, and then they'll have to let her go. You understand that?"

I found my voice. "Yes, I understand. And I know the judge and the lawyers will have to hustle."

"I know this plan might seem extreme," he went on, "but if it happens that your mother has to have police intervention and be taken to the hospital for an eval, at least her care will be in the hands of doctors, not in that incompetent lawyer's."

On our way home we stopped by assisted living and told them they were to call the police department if Mom tried to leave. I hastily wrote a letter to that effect, slid it through their copier, and left the original with the receptionist. They were more than willing to cooperate. At long last, they, too, had not only the desire but the means to protect Mom.

I called the ombudsman again when we got home and told him about the plan. "She's going to hate this," he said, "and hate you for it, but it'll be like a two-year-old throwing a tantrum. She won't understand that you are acting in her best interest. Right now, her paranoia is making her want to flee."

He then suggested that I call Senior Protective Services, which I did as soon as we hung up. A representative told me that unless a crime was in progress or had already been committed, there was nothing they could do for us. And it was true; no one was committing any crimes against Mom. Not yet, anyway.

Fifty-five

When we got home I called Mom's friend, the one who was helping her move. She was Mom's old golf partner in her nine-hole group at the country club. While Mom was in Utah she had received cards and notes from this friend wishing her well on her new life there.

I had come across this correspondence when trying to sort through all of Mom's messes at the Utah house. "I hardly know her," she had said at the time. "I have no intention of replying to her. I don't know why she bothers. Just throw her letters out."

But when Mom reached the peak of frustration at the assisted living facility, she reached out to anyone who would listen. This friend was a widow and about eight years younger than Mom. I only knew her first name. I mentally chastised myself for not keeping a copy of her full name and address. I had no idea how to contact her, but a conversation with a friend of my own from high school gave me a lead.

My friend lived in southern Oregon, and we communicated from time to time. Her mother was showing symptoms of dementia, but had not yet been officially diagnosed with Alzheimer's. In my rage and frustration I called her one day and told her about the legal system and how hard it was to protect my mother. I also told her about Mom's plans.

Through an odd quirk of fate, she knew Mom's friend and her daughter, and it happened that the following weekend the daughter was going to be in Oregon visiting her. She called again and introduced us.

I explained to the daughter Mom's health conditions and asked her if I could give her mother a call and, hopefully, get her to understand my mother's situation.

The next night Mom's friend and I spent almost four hours on the phone. But first my friend called: Mom's friend had phoned her to ask about my character.

"Apparently your mother bad-mouthed you to the women's golf group at the club, so she thinks you're a pretty trashy person. I think I set her straight. I told her about my relationship with you and how wonderful you are." I thanked her fervently.

And indeed my mother had filled her friend and the other nine-hole ladies with all the evil things I had done, or that Mom said I had done, especially since I declined to attend Mom and Dad's fiftieth anniversary party at the club. I was considered part of the criminal class by the ladies of the club. Poor Lila; to have a daughter like me must be such a burden.

Mom told them I always borrowed money and never paid her back. That I was reckless in my relationships, that I was an awful welfare mother who had moved to Oregon only to cover up my bad behavior. No family members or friends from California could ever see how I really did turn out, since I was hiding in Oregon. Mom told the ladies that even my own brother was through with me.

"Your mother had nothing good to say about you, so I'm skeptical, although my daughter's friend says that you are a good person," Mom's friend told me when we first got on the phone.

"I've had no doubt that Mom has been painting me as the enemy every chance she gets. And I admit that she and I have had our differences. But she's very sick now. She needs help, and that's what I'm trying to do, help her and keep her safe."

We talked about Mom's move to Utah.

"We all told her not to go," the friend said. "Or at least wait for a while and think about it and spend some time there to see what Utah had to offer her and Jim. We all knew your Dad was not a healthy man. He used to be a scratch golfer, but we all saw him decline over the years."

"Mom told me that everyone down there wished her well and said the move to Utah was a brilliant idea. She claimed that my brother wished her well too, but I know that in reality he told her it was a foolish idea. She kept hounding him for approval, so he gave up trying to reason with her and told her 'good luck.' From those two words, she came to the conclusion that he supported this move.

"We were unanimous as a family in telling her not to go. We pointed out that she and Dad would be far away from her family, and that they couldn't make it on their own. My brother spent twenty-five years watching out for them, you know. I moved to Oregon in seventy-nine, but he was always there to take care of them. He put in new water heaters, fixed their cars and their plumbing, and cleaned out their rain gutters for years and years. Meanwhile, I was up here. I rarely saw them, and if I did, it was only for lunch or dinner. I just couldn't stand their constant fighting," I admitted.

"But now it's my turn to step up and offer care. Greg has had enough, and I'm pretty fed up myself with her foolish decisions. Please don't encourage her anymore and please don't help her with any plan. There is no way she can live on her own. I'm terrified of what would happen to her if she tried."

By the end of the conversation, the friend had agreed to bow out of my mother's affairs and let the court and the lawyers and Mom's doctors do what was best for her to keep her safe and protected.

Mom's friend and I had several more conversations. I had to keep repeating things I'd already told her, so I wondered if she was having her own memory problems. My aim was to make sure that she fully realized that Mom was very sick.

"I have my grandson stay with me every summer," the woman told me during one of our conversations. "He's twelve, so my summers with him are very important. Pretty soon he'll stop coming. He'll get involved with his own activities."

I saw this as an opening to bring my point home. "You should know that Mom can get quite violent." I told her about Mom's attempt to strike me in the doctor's office. I told her about Mom coming face-to-face with the toddler in Utah. And then I told her about how Dad had died. She was horrified.

I pressed ahead to further make my case. "If Mom manages to get to California, she'll have no way to get her medications. She's on some strong antipsychotic drugs, and there's no telling how she'll be once she's off those meds."

"Oh dear ..." Mom's friend said, her voice trailing off.

"Do you have wine in your house?" I asked.

"Well yes, I have a glass now and then."

"Mom loves to chug her medications with a tall glass of Carlo Rossi. Think about this, are you prepared to take care of her if she overdoses on wine and drugs?"

I heard Mom's friend take in a deep breath. I hoped she was thinking about her grandson suffering the presence of an old lady who drank, abused medications, and could be mean to children.

"Lord. What do I do if she shows up at my doorstep?"

"Chances of that are pretty slim. She gets lost easily and I doubt she'd make it. Plus we're monitoring her all the time, the staff at her facility and me. We will certainly know if she disappears. If by some chance she does show up at your door, though, call me and I'll come and get her. I can be at your house in ten hours if I drive, or less if I fly."

We ended the phone call with her assurance that she would stay out of my mother's life.

We waited and waited for the legal world to push the paperwork forward to grant conservatorship to my brother Greg. He and I had marathon phone conversations. I called and told him about Mom's friend and her attempts to help Mom move to a motel. Fortunately, there was no word from the Corvallis Police Department and the facility never had to call to tell me Mom had disappeared.

"Ya know," Greg said, "other than you, no one asked me to be Mom's conservator. Not her attorney, not your attorney, not the judge, and not Mom. I haven't talked to her in more than a year, and that conversation ended badly."

The last time Greg and Mom had spoken was Mother's Day, 2006. Greg called to wish her a happy day and she went on a rampage about how much she hated her life and how I had screwed things up for her. She demanded that she and Dad live with him. Greg told her, "Now wait a minute, before you go making any plans you should talk to your doctors about ..."

Mom hung up on him, but not before he heard her telling Dad, "Greg doesn't want us either." Greg continued to send birthday and holiday greeting cards, but Mom never contacted him again. That she would now be overjoyed to have him control every penny of her money was pretty unlikely.

"And no one has investigated me like they did you," Greg went on. "I could be some schmuck with a criminal background and evil intent. In fact, you and I could be setting this whole thing up to leave Mom destitute, but no one in the legal field ever bothered to see if I was even interested or if I was qualified. For all they know, I could be in Asia or in Africa. The only reason I'm doing this at all is because you asked me to."

More than three weeks after the meeting in my lawyer's office, my brother finally received the letters of conservatorship. As soon as that happened, I called assisted living.

In order to manage her money, I had to know the status of her finances. I could hardly demand she give me her checkbook and purse without literally risking her life. Mom had had that second aneurysm, she had a history of TIAs, and no way, no how would I provoke her into having a heart attack or stroke.

Now that I had the legal means to confiscate Mom's financial resources, I hatched a plan to raid her apartment. I knew that she would know I'd done it. She'd notice that some of her piles of paperwork were missing and think of me first. But this way, I could avoid a heated confrontation.

Doug and I sat in our car in the parking lot waiting for a call from the receptionist at Mom's facility. She would let us know when Mom had left her apartment and was in the dining room. Doug and I were armed with bags and boxes with which to haul off every scrap of paper. It would have to be a fast expedition. We were both on our lunch hour, and we had to get back to work.

The cell phone rang and the receptionist told us that Mom was in her seat at her table in the dining room. She met us at the side door, which was always locked, and let us in. I still had a key to Mom's apartment, so in we went. We were there only a few minutes before we heard a key turning the lock in the door. We quickly ran to the bathroom and hid. If caught, I was prepared to stroll out of the bathroom and pretend to have been looking for her, but she soon returned to the dining room.

My cell phone rang: it was the receptionist. "Sorry. Your mom wanted her sweater. The coast is clear for a little while."

We had brought a camera because Mom's apartment was unbelievable. We photographed every room, every closet, and every corner. If anyone questioned why we had done what we did, the photographs would help support our claim that my mother was incapable of managing her own life.

Doug and I scooped up armfuls of paperwork and dumped them into the bags and boxes. We grabbed every piece of paper we could find, knowing Mom's habit of hiding things inside other things: bank statements in the junk mail and hundred-dollar bills inside paper napkins. I opened every drawer and grabbed all the paper I could find, including newspapers, catalogs, and magazines.

I also took all of her many purses, not sure which one she was using at present. Since she had no legal control over her money anymore, I wanted to make sure we had her checkbooks, credit cards, and any other links to her assets.

As soon as we returned to our car, I called the receptionist to let her know we had left. I didn't hear from Mom for five days; then I found a message from her on our answering machine: five words.

"I know you were here."

Doug and I spent days and days sorting through all we had brought home. Once again we triaged Mom's paperwork: what to keep, what to recycle, and what to throw away. At least now we knew this would be the last time. We might not have all of it, but once we did, it would be out of her hands for good.

The next morning I got a phone call from a teller at Mom's bank.

"Your mother has an overdraft of over six thousand dollars made payable to a coin collector in New York. This is an electronic check, so she gave them the routing numbers to her account," the teller said. "I called your mother to ask how she wanted to handle this overdraft. She said to roll her ninety-thousand-dollar money market account over into her checking account. That's a lot of money, and I know you have power of attorney, so I thought I should call."

I explained that my brother had just been granted letters of conservatorship from the court and we had not yet contacted the bank.

"Right now, we're trying to sort through all of her paperwork so we can understand what we're dealing with," I said. "This checking account, when I was managing it last year, had over fifty thousand dollars in it. Please just move over enough money to cover Mom's overdrafts and no more.

I called Greg, who had just received the court-issued documents for his conservatorship in the mail. He planned to go to one of Mom's bank branches that morning.

When he got back, he called me. "Bad news, I'm afraid. I talked to a banker who said that she had doubts that a conservatorship would work in this case. Mom and Dad had a trust, and even though Mom never put any assets in it, she gave the bank a copy. The banker called their legal department to double-check on this, but conservatorship doesn't trump a trust—this conservatorship is no good. We can't cancel or change Mom's accounts even though the court gave us permission."

After I hung up the phone I put my head in my hands. All the time and effort we'd put into getting this conservatorship—and all of it a waste.

I called the banker at the local branch in Corvallis and shared the bad news. She had been wonderful to us, helpful all along the way, calling me each time Mom or her lawyer came in to see how Mom's finances were doing. She had worked at an Alzheimer's home while putting herself through college, so she knew about dementia diseases. When they had been unable to find a trace of Mom's Utah annuity and her lawyer had said publicly that I should be arrested for embezzlement, she'd advised, "You should sue him for slander."

Now her hands were tied. According to the bank's legal staff, they couldn't allow us to close Mom's accounts and re-open a new one with my brother as her conservator. There was no way we could protect her by controlling her money. This was the sum of all of our hard work: not one step forward without the approval of the banking world. It seemed as though Mom's universe was just as it always was, impossible to penetrate, by legal or moral means.

For almost a week Doug and I drove to and from work with hardly a word spoken between us. We were utterly defeated, and had only a single conversation about it.

"I guess I'll have to give Mom back her credit cards and check-books," I said.

"I can't believe it was all for nothing," Doug replied.

Fifty-six

One afternoon as I was about to leave work, I got a call from Mom's local banker.

"Stop by my office before you go home," was all she said.

Doug and I walked into the bank to find her sitting at her desk grinning. She was holding up a legal document.

"What's this?" she asked me, handing it over.

"It looks like a copy of my parents' trust."

"And guess what: you are their trustee!" she said, a huge smile on her lovely face.

"A trustee can appoint a conservator, and then a conservator can appoint a designee, so you and Greg are covered. And by the way, I already called your brother with the good news. But I made him promise that I would be the one who got to tell you."

We had been saved by the kindness and diligence of an angel, one of many who reside side by side with us, we who need help from unforeseen resources.

Greg took the extra step and researched Oregon law online; sure enough, all he had to do was write a letter appointing me as his designee. He sent me copies. Now, because of a legal decision she had made long ago to set up a trust, we were both Mom's caregivers. When the court issued the letters of conservatorship, Mom would be considered an incapacitated person, not capable of managing her financial affairs.

Greg closed Mom's two bank accounts: her checking and her money market/savings account. He opened new accounts for her in his name as conservator. He signed a whole checkbook's worth of checks and sent them to me. At last I was in full control of my mother's life. I finally had all I needed to keep her safe.

Fifty-seven

By early August Mom was still at assisted living, but there was a new director in charge. I hadn't liked him from the moment we met; he seemed slippery to me, and a little too glib considering the responsibility of his position. He had been director for a couple of months now.

One day he called to announce he was going to take Mom golfing.

The insanity of this idea was immediately obvious. "Oh really?" I said, "I have a different idea. I would suggest that you stay out of my mother's life. She has severe osteoporosis, she has an aneurysm on her aorta, and she's a flight risk, which is well documented in your own records. If you took the time to look at them, you'd find many reports of her leaving with strangers, with you having no idea where she went. I would also suggest that you pay attention to running your business and stop trying to be a comic-book hero to my mother. If I ever hear that you have removed her from that facility, I will sic my lawyer on you, and your corporation."

Shortly thereafter, he called again while I was at work. This was about an entirely different matter.

"You have to move your mother to another facility," he said. "A housekeeper told me that your mother has flammable items stacked in front of her zonal heater in her apartment."

"Yes, I know. I've moved those items many times, and she keeps moving them back."

"If a fire started there, not only would your mother not be able to get past it to the door, it could move through the whole building. You have to move her."

"OK, I'll call her doctors and see what I can do."

During the ordeal of establishing conservatorship, I had put moving Mom to a memory-care facility in the back of my mind. There had been too much activity, too much stress—too much of everything—to tackle that subject too. Now it was time for me to step up and deal with it.

I called her primary physician, who told me he could discuss such a move with me without her being present. Then I went to the facility that was closest to where she was currently living and talked to the marketing director. She looked quite skeptical when I told her how extreme my mother's behavior had become, but she was a professional and knew how to get the ball rolling to move her as soon as possible.

"I know your mother's doctor," she said. "I'll make sure he has signed all of the paperwork."

Next I worked with the business manager at this facility to get Mom's monthly bills set up for automatic electronic payment. From there, I went to another facility that specialized in adult day care for those who were affected by memory-loss problems or physical disabilities. I made an arrangement to have my mother there on August 17, the day she would move from assisted living to the memory-loss facility.

"Hey, Mom," I said. "I know how bored and lonely you are, so I set up a date for you at this new daytime center in town. Maybe you can meet some friends there. And even if you're not interested in that, the staff is wonderful and they'll have things for you to do."

Mom shrugged her shoulders. She was back to her angry old self. "So when am I moving to California?"

"Mom, you can't move. Your lawyer offered conservatorship of you. Your doctors have diagnosed you with Alzheimer's. You're staying here."

"I do not have Alzheimer's. I don't feel sick at all. I don't feel like I have Alzheimer's."

I let that one pass. "I'll pick you up Friday morning and we'll go to this new place."

"I'm moving to California, you know, and you can't stop me."

"Mom, you should never have left San Jose." I couldn't let them all pass.

"But we had a house in Utah."

"Yes, I've heard that before."

"I want my purse and my checkbook."

"Mom, I can't do that. You and your lawyer chose this plan, and now that the judge has approved it, we can't change it unless you can prove that you're being abused, either physically or financially. And you're not. I will see you on Friday."

On the drive home I thought about all the damage Mom's lawyer had done. Lobbying for her independence. Insisting on and then concealing a second opinion. Ignoring her financial picture—even when she was overdue on payments for his own fees. Even bullying the staff at the assisted living facility, insisting she didn't have Alzheimer's and that they were medicating her incorrectly. Not once did he ever review Mom's medical records.

But worst of all, he had promised my mother a life that was not available to her. Clinging to what she wanted to hear, she fully believed that I was the only roadblock to her dream of freedom and autonomy.

Unbelievably, this lawyer's firm specialized in estate planning, wills, and trusts. He must have known that I was my parents' trustee and we could appoint a conservator who would control Mom's finances a hundred percent.

It was when I talked to my lawyer about initiating a malpractice suit against Mom's attorney that I learned how the world of small-town lawyers works: they do not sue one another. I would have to go as far away as Seattle or San Francisco to find a law firm that could help me. After everything we'd been through, and knowing what we still had to do to take care of Mom, as angry as I was about the wreckage that Mom's attorney had wrought in our lives, I knew that there would be no such suit.

I knew that one day I would calm down. Time and distance away from any nerve-wracking situation was the best medicine for me. My lawyer and his staff were doing their best to help me protect my mother. Mom's lawyer was perhaps inexperienced enough to believe that he was on his white horse protecting her from her grasping daughter. Other people had believed the untruths that Mom had said about me. But in the end, he handed her to us by giving us full control over all of her assets, which allowed us to be in charge of her life and protect her from harm.

The part that I found to be unforgivable, that I knew that I could never reconcile, was the second opinion that her lawyer had demanded. This second opinion should have raised many red flags for my mother's legal advisor to see. As far as I knew, he never considered her medical history. And to accuse me of tainting my mother's diagnosis was, and always will be, beyond my comprehension. There was no way I could influence an MRI, nor could I influence the outcomes of Mom's MMSEs or her doctors' conclusions. Alzheimer's was a permanent member in our family, an unwanted relative who would never leave us until Mom passed away.

I can only hope that any lawyer will look closely at their client's medical records before proclaiming that a person is healthy enough to live independently, especially in a case resembling mine, when a primary care physician, a neurologist, a mental health specialist, a registered nurse, and professional care providers all documented that my mother was a flight risk and a danger to herself and others because of her dementia disease, Alzheimer's.

Fifty-eight

The Friday of Mom's move, Doug drove our truck to the assisted living facility and I followed him there in our car. He waited in the parking lot while I got Mom into my car and we drove off to the adult day care center. I knew that Mom would never recognize our truck, so she would never see Doug. She didn't look around anymore, only stared forward. As a result of flat affect, her face could no longer show any expression at all.

One sign of flat affect is the inability to make eye contact, but Mom had spent her life avoiding eye contact. That's why I hadn't recognized the onset of that particular symptom. Again, it continued to be hard to know when Mom was being Mom and when Alzheimer's and extreme paranoia were at work.

Once at the day care center, she would not have to witness the next big event in her life, not until we picked her up that afternoon. I had lied to her about it—I didn't know how to tell her she was moving to a lockdown memory-care facility. I had so hoped that Mom would settle into her life in assisted living; it was so plush and had so many activities, and they took such good care of her and Dad—that is, when Mom let them. But her manic episodes and escalating violence meant that she could no longer live unsupervised.

Doug had Mom's key, so he let himself into her apartment after we left. Our plan was to get the things she needed moved over to the memory-loss facility: her bed, dresser, nightstand, desk, recliner, end table, clothes, and other necessary items. We had until 3:30 to do all of this before we had to pick her up.

I was terribly nervous. My heart broke for Mom. She could have had a really nice life where she was. But the escape attempts, her unsafe behavior, what she did to Dad, and all the money she lost snuffed out that hope. She was eighty-nine and would be in a memory-care facility for the rest of her life. Alzheimer's changed everything.

Driving Mom to day care was fairly simple. She was quite complacent and let me guide her into the facility. I introduced her to the staff and found a place for her to sit. In the kitchen they were making pineapple upside down cake for midday dessert. "See you this afternoon, Mom. Have fun here today," I said as I left.

Back at Mom's apartment, I found Doug standing in the middle of the living room.

"Sorry," he said. "I know I need to get moving, but I actually don't know where to begin." He turned three-sixty with his arm outstretched. "Where does one start?"

I walked over and stood next to him.

"I've been standing here since you left," he told me. "I honestly don't know what to do."

We were both devastated that we had to do this yet again, never having quite recovered from the multiple times we'd cleaned up after her before. We had been sure that things would be under control for her in assisted living, but here we were again cleaning up Mom's fundamentally unbelievable mess. We took photographs, positive that no one would believe what we were dealing with—still, and again.

"Maybe we should start by opening a window and turning off the heater," Doug offered.

"OK," I said, glad for any suggestion. "I bought new sheets, mattress pad, towels, and other bedding. All that stuff is in the car, so we don't need to find any of that. We can strip Mom's bed and put the mattress, headboard, box spring, and bed frame in the truck. Then we haul her chair down. After that ... I don't know. Her dressers are filled with junk and garbage and her clothes are strewn here and there. We have to empty all of the dressers, find things she needs, and then pack them into the dressers. Right?"

"But where does one start?" Doug repeated. Then he slowly got in motion.

In some places, we were hip deep in shipping boxes that had never been opened; stuffed animals, books, magazines, and catalogs were everywhere. And we fully knew we had to sort through everything—veterans of too many treasure hunts by now. Mom's wedding ring had gone missing again. I had once taken it to a local jeweler for repair and knew it was appraised at more than three thousand dollars.

More importantly, this ring had stones in it from Mom's original wedding ring and from my grandmother's ring. During one of his tours of duty in Vietnam, my brother had bought several more stones, and she had added these, so it was a family history ring now. In Utah I had found it in an office trash can in one of the spare bedrooms, in one of those small plastic containers you'd find in a fast food place for ketchup or hot sauce.

We couldn't reach her dressers—there was too much stuff barricading them—so we dug in, opening one box after another. "Would you look at this?!" Doug said, finding a tanzanite stone wrapped inside an invoice for four hundred and eleven dollars.

Candy was everywhere. We stepped on it and sat on it and smelled it and threw it at each other, and all the while the clock was ticking. We had to allow enough time to move Mom's things to her new place and have it all set up for her before I picked her up. By noon we were tired, dirty, and frustrated. We had filled the facility's dumpster, so we started just bagging up trash and garbage and setting it against a wall in the bedroom.

Mom had turned Dad's twin bed into a storage unit. Shipping boxes were piled high on top and underneath. Where does one begin, indeed?

I sorted her clothes and packed things for indoor living, knowing that she would probably never go outside again except to walk to a car. Doug removed her Bose stereo and most of her wall art. Several days earlier we had bought her a new TV at Costco. It was the perfect size for Mom's new place, and it had a built-in DVD player. The cable TV company told us Mom's service was all set up for her at the new place.

By early afternoon Doug and I were moving like tree sloths. We stopped for a water break. To the right of the small kitchen was the apartment's vestibule. The entry door was propped open with a painted rock—some kitten scene—so we could get some air circulating. We were surprised to see three sweet faces peeking inside, some of the residents from the same wing.

"Oh, hi," I said.

"We tried to make friends with her," one of them said.

"Yes, I 'm sure you did. She was hard to get to know."

"She would stand at her door and wait, and make your dad wait, too, when he was still here," another one said. "She'd wait until everyone had gone into their rooms before she would open her door."

"And she always walked behind us when we went down to the dining room," said another. "She would never stay for the games or the songs or just to visit."

I thanked them for trying to be my mother's friends. They said they were sorry that she had to move. When we carried our last load into the truck, the same three ladies were sitting in comfortable lounge chairs on the huge front porch.

"We weren't sure you'd get it all in," one of them said. "She sure had a lot of stuff!"

To say that was an understatement would have been an understatement.

Mom was leaving a seven-hundred-square-foot apartment—one bedroom; one bathroom; living room; kitchen with a fridge, microwave, sink, and cabinets; large entryway; two small closets; and one huge walk-in closet that could have been a small office or bedroom—and moving into a one-room place with a sink and a shared bathroom, one of those Jack-and-Jill setups. She had complained bitterly about having to live nose-to-nose with my dad. I was sure that she would hate the new place.

It was after 2:30 now, and we still had to drive to the memory-loss facility, unload Mom's things, and set up her room. As soon as we arrived, several staff members came and offered to help us unload the truck and get the room ready. At 3:15 I excused myself to go pick her up.

Mom had never paid any attention to the direction I drove, or where we were going. She didn't notice that I wasn't driving toward her apartment. I pulled into the portico area of her new, and probably last, home.

"Mom," I said as we were walking in the door to the reception area, "this is going to be your new home. The staff members are waiting to meet you."

Flat affect or not, Mom looked angry and suspicious, and rightly so. I had blindsided her. I had lied to her and planned her life behind her back. And I reminded myself that if I could do this so easily, any predator could too. The decision had been a painful one to make, but I knew it was the right one.

At the far side of the reception area was a set of double doors that led to the residences. To get through those doors you had to type in a four-digit code and press a button. A green light turned on to let you know that, for a few seconds, the doors were unlocked. If someone tried to force the door, or if it was left open for too long, an alarm would sound. This was lockdown; once you were inside, under the orders of a primary care physician, you could not be released. Mom had passed the point in her life when she could still come and go as she pleased.

I guided Mom to her new room, which looked very nice. Doug and the staff had been busy. All of the wall art was up, the dresser was full, the bed made, clothes and toiletries put away, and the room was clean. Mom sat in a chair looked at the strange faces that smiled and greeted her.

She was not happy. She was bunching up her shoulders and clenching her fists.

Standing outside were the marketing director and the office manager. A chef from the kitchen came in and introduced himself. The registered nurse also came in. As they moved toward Mom, Doug and I were being slowly squeezed to the back of the crowd. It appeared they had practiced this drill before. The office manager quietly said to me, "Time for you to leave now. We will take it from here. Call tomorrow, and we'll give you an update."

We were nearly through the door and into the hall when I heard my mother's voice. "Karen?"

I had been doing all right until then, but the sound of her small voice somewhere past the crowd of staff broke the dam. I cried and cried, sobbing all the way to the car. I felt so guilty. I wished that there could be another way, any other way, to take care of her.

Doug and I were so tired. All the years of taking care of Mom and Dad, the way Dad had died, the legal battles, the crushing responsibility of putting my mother's scattered life back together had all been overwhelming. And now this, the lovely guilt. I felt utterly shattered.

The director of the facility told me to stay away for a while—maybe two weeks—so Mom could adjust to her new surroundings without me. "If you're here each day, all she'll focus on is pressuring you to move her somewhere else. She needs to settle into her new life."

I surrendered to the voice of experience.

Fifty-nine

Guilt aside, the prospect of having a life of our own for two weeks was great, but we knew what was waiting for us back at Mom's apartment. We had the rest of the weekend to clean out her things, and we both had to be back to work on Monday.

The next morning we drove to Mom's apartment in our three-quarter-ton farm truck, a GMC long bed with an extended cab. We were armed with trash bags and boxes from U-Haul, a shop vac, gloves, and dust masks.

"Let's start with the fridge and the kitchen stuff," I suggested.

"At least we can open the windows and let out that awful smell," Doug said.

We gagged and held our noses and filled three garbage bags with old food from the fridge and freezer. There was food there in a to-go box from the restaurant we had gone to eighteen months before, for Thanksgiving. Neither one of us was brave enough to open it. Several staff members stopped by to say, "We tried to clean this place, but she wouldn't let us in." We knew the mess wasn't their fault. We hugged them and thanked them for their efforts.

By early afternoon the awful smells were history, and now we were starving. We made our first trip to the landfill and the recycling center and stopped downtown to grab some fast food, and then we were back at it. By about ten o'clock that night we were tired, cranky, and dirty—and not finished. We locked the apartment and drove home.

We were more hopeful the next day, thinking we had made progress, but when we entered Mom's apartment we were confronted by the remaining heaps and mounds of materials we still had to haul out. It was mind-numbing. We both felt exhausted, and it was only eight in the morning.

By late Sunday night, though, we were relieved to see that Mom's old apartment was sparkling clean. In two days we had hauled away eight pickup loads, each time filling our truck's three-quarter-ton bed all the way up to the cab.

As soon as the last item was stuffed into the truck, I went back into Mom and Dad's apartment, looking one more time to see if we'd left anything behind. I thought about this now-deserted place, about the promise of an empty room. The sounds and aromas, the furnishings and colors, the secrets that would be told there, the love—all that a room, a home, can offer the people who live there.

What we dreaded sorting through most were the shipments that had filled Mom's apartment. We found boxes from more than a dozen vendors. For some unknown reason, whenever she received a box, she removed the packing slip from the plastic sleeves on the outside. Now we had hundreds of boxes with no identification, unmatched to the invoices we had found mixed in, seemingly at random, with junk mail and catalogs. We wanted to return as many of these items as we could, and didn't look forward to the scavenger hunt involved in matching goods with paperwork.

We also had Mom's coins to contend with. Some were worthless, just plated commemorative coins, but some were the real thing. At face value all the coins amounted to $12,000; we wanted to return these too.

Greg was now monitoring all of Mom's accounts, and he was finally able to assure us that all of her old checks had cleared the bank. Her last order of coins was the biggest problem for us. She had ordered these by providing the old routing numbers. The company had pulled $2,700 from her old account, and when that payment bounced, we had to cover those charges by moving money from her money market account to check so we had proof that this payment had been covered by Mom's bank.

In trying to return that $2,700 order, I found that I'd gotten pretty good at dealing with potential predators. The guy on the phone claimed Mom had written a check for the coins, which had bounced. I had the electronic records and knew this wasn't true, and told him so, thinking that was the end of it. When he called a few days later, still insisting that payment hadn't come through, I had had enough.

"Well now, you listen to me, you little creep," I said, "Mom paid that bill and I can prove it, and maybe you'd like to guess what I'm doing right now. I'm online looking for the listing for the DA's office in your area. As soon as we're finished here I'm going to make a call and initiate charges against you, for elderly financial abuse and for—" Click. I didn't get to finish, and I never heard from him again. My anger over the incident ebbed, and after a while all I felt was relief that no one would ever be able to exploit her again.

We moved all of Mom's purchases to her storage unit, intending to spend some warm summer evenings there boxing them up for return. But all the years of caregiving had worn us down, and we never seemed to get to it. Mom's mystery packages continued to sit among her treasures as summer came and went.

As the days turned cold and the nights grew longer we decided that the only way to accomplish this huge task was to haul everything to our house. At least there we could work from the comfort of our living room, even though we were reluctant to invite Mom's chaos into our home. We sent back clocks, watches, wall art, vases, children's toys, women's cheap shoes, Elvis Presley and Betty Boop Christmas ornaments, and authentic American Indian art and artifacts sporting the label "Made in Vietnam." There was so much of it that when we took it to the post office we were asked to use the loading dock. We did this every weekday for two full weeks.

All in all, we recovered almost seventeen thousand dollars and deposited it into Mom and Greg's checking account.

I wrote close to thirty letters to various vendors and junk mailers as I sifted through the litter, telling them to stop sending their come-ons. Again I used the threat of the DA's office, and most of the companies stopped. But others started mailing things to to me at my address, and I had to start my letter writing campaign all over, this time threatening to sue them for harassment. Eventually we reclaimed our home and our mailbox as our own.

The rest of Mom's things would stay in the storage unit, most of it from her family and things she had acquired when her brain was still her friend—but there was still a small mountain of junk. It's probably just as well that I didn't yet know it would take me three more years to clear everything out.

Going through the last bag of trash that I found in one of the two-drawer filing cabinets, we discovered Delores's lost watch. This plastic trash bag contained soiled napkins, candy wrappers, a dirty t-shirt, a broken clip-on earring, and some empty paper coffee cups. Inside one of the stained cups was the watch.

"What do we do with it now?" Doug asked. Neither one of us had an answer. I also found, filed away, the cards and letters that I had sent to Mom offering to cook and clean while she recovered from her open-heart surgery. Mom's case had been settled and there was no one, and no point, in trying to show these items to anyone.

Sixty

When Doug and I went back to see Mom again after the prescribed time, she was furious. As we left, she got physical, pounding on the locked doors, shouting for us to come back and get her out of there. "I am moving and you cannot stop me!" came the familiar refrain.

I started visiting her solo. The director told me to limit my visits to just a few minutes, and it was easy to agree. Mom would get so upset when she saw me that I feared her aneurysm would burst or she'd have a heart attack or a stroke, or maybe slip and fall while hurrying after me. At least I knew she was safe now and even though she was obsessed with fleeing the place, it was impossible.

One day the director called me. "Hi, Karen. A woman who claims to be a friend of your mother's from California has been calling me . . . And I have some things I think you should see."

The next day the director laid out on a conference table the contents of an envelope that Mom's old conspiring friend had sent her. There were motel brochures, real estate ads, car ads, phone numbers for attorneys and real estate agents—all in San Jose—as well as Amtrak and Greyhound bus schedules.

"What the...?"

"Karen, this woman has told me that she doesn't believe your mother has Alzheimer's. She's convinced that she's here without justification—that you've imprisoned her for no reason. After speaking with her, I had the staff search your mother's room while she was at lunch. They brought me as much as they could find."

She gave me some time to look at everything Mom's friend had sent. "I had a long, long phone conversation with this woman about Mom's condition, and before we hung up she agreed not to do this anymore," I said, shaking my head, my voice wobbling.

The director offered me a box of tissues.

"I don't understand this. How did Mom get all this stuff?"

"Since you are not her guardian, she still has the right to receive her own mail. It would be easy enough for her friend to find our address—we have a website."

I had wondered when our lack of guardian status would come back to bite us.

"And I'm afraid this isn't the only thing I need to talk with you about. I also need to let you know that your mother has become very aggressive. She's been hitting the staff members—not hard, just slaps on the arm, and they can take it. The problem is, if your mother should hit or push one of our other residents she could hurt them." She gestured toward the residences. "This place is filled with fragile people."

I thought of tiny Mom at a hundred pounds pushing Dad, who weighed 250. She had also pushed Kristen when she came to see her. As Kristen was leaving after a trying visit, she said, "Be happy, Grandma, please just try to be happy"—the exact same words Margaret had used in Utah. Infuriated by this, for reasons only Mom would ever know, she pushed my daughter, a marathoner and all-around athlete, who nearly fell.

I made appointments for Mom with her primary care physician and her neurologist. The memory-care facility had faxed over notes documenting my mother's aggressive behavior and that she never came out of her room, that she refused to bathe, that she refused staff-supplied services, that she accused people of coming into her room and stealing her things.

The doctors conferred and put Mom on a new antipsychotic drug and an antidepressant. "These will take a few weeks to start working," I was told. "And she'll need to take them in ever-increasing dosages. But they should help to calm her down without making her comatose." Still, I worried about overmedicating my Mom.

Another call from the director came in. "Karen, that woman from San Jose has been calling again. It looks like she and your mother have hatched a plan—your mother says her friend is on her way to get her."

"That ain't gonna to happen," I immediately responded.

"She's in her eighties. I doubt that her family would let her take a long road trip by herself, and I know she's never been to Oregon. The whole trip would probably freak her out. Mom's not telling the truth."

"I kind of figured that. I told the woman that because of her actions your mother has lost her phone privileges. My aides have removed the phone and the phone book from your mother's room. And the newspapers. I suggest that you cancel her subscription. All she does is shop for lawyers, real estate agents, and cars."

"Consider it done."

"Good. Your mother needs to adjust as best she can to her new world here. The newspapers don't help."

Two days later I took Mom to another doctor's appointment. While we were gone, Doug went to her room and removed all of the pens, pencils, and writing tablets, and her personal phone directory. He even took the ribbon out of her typewriter. It pained both of us to see her world shrinking that way, but we knew tough love was called for. It had been clear for years now that nothing good ever came of her ability to reach the outside world.

I copied all of the materials Mom's friend had sent her and wrote her a letter, copying my lawyer. I threatened legal action if she ever interfered again with my mother's care and protection. I now knew her promise to stop butting in had been an empty one, and I could only hope that at her age she didn't relish a legal battle.

I kept visiting Mom on a regular basis. Each time it was awful. I always brought a small gift: flowers, a magazine, or a new *TV Guide*. The most successful gifts were a couple of coffees: house coffee with cream on the side and a mocha. I started bringing them more often.

We spent some time with her at Christmas and she had very little to say. I was getting all her mail now, and I picked out some Christmas cards for her to read, hoping that none of them would be inflammatory. They seemed to cheer her up a bit. I was happy that people still remembered her and made the effort to be in touch. Finally, there was one kind of outside contact with Mom that I didn't have to fear, the cards and letters from her friends and family, who loved her.

Sixty-one

In February 2008, Doug and I were on our way to Ashland. It would be a short, overnight visit: dinner, a play, motel, and home the next day. On I-5 near Roseburg my cell phone rang. It was the memory-care facility.

"Karen, we think that your mother needs to see a doctor."

"Is it an emergency?"

"No, not yet. But I just learned she's refusing to eat. In the last few days she's lost eight pounds. That's a lot for her. She's now down to ninety-two pounds."

I called and set up a doctor's appointment for Mom for the following week. The facility staff told me they were putting protein powder in the small amounts of soup she would eat and into drinks like Ensure or chocolate milkshakes when they could talk her into having one.

We saw the doctor on call. Mom was obviously in pain but she gave no indication of where the pain was located. The doctor saw that Mom had a curve in her lower back and ordered X-rays.

"She has a severely curved spine from osteoporosis," the doctor said. "It's a sideways curve like you see with scoliosis. It does not help that she sits most of the time."

The doctor had Mom pull up her shirt a bit so we could see the curve of her lower back. It didn't look good.

"We try to get her to get up and walk around—the staff, that is, and me when I'm there—but she sits in her chair all day, sometimes slumped to one side or the other."

She had been tuning us out as usual, but Mom suddenly came back into the room and looked straight into the doctor's eyes. "I really don't want to live anymore."

I was surprised by her abrupt return to reality, but not by what she had declared. I knew she was miserable.

The doctor addressed the only problem he could solve, prescribing an oral dose of morphine for her back. After her pain subsided in a couple of days, she could receive back rubs of a topical medication for the pain. He also recommended that I get hospice involved.

"Hospice can help her with her pain, and perhaps her depression," he said. "Hospice isn't just for end-of-life care. They can help immensely with quality-of-life care too."

Soon Mom's room became a whirlwind of busy-ness, with hospice personnel coming and going. She was quite the challenge for them. They made suggestions that I had made many times before, and I knew she wouldn't heed them. They told me to bring her DVDs, CDs, puzzles, and writing material.

I told them all about my mother: how my dad had died, how Mom would escape if given a chance, and on and on I went. Each hospice worker seemed dubious, probably thinking I was exaggerating if not imagining things. Mom was, after all, tiny, and she could be cute and charming when she wanted to be.

On the days and times the hospice people were there, I stayed away. I wanted her to have the benefit of at least trying their services and I didn't want to be accused again of tainting people's opinions about Mom. So I let them find her as she was.

Early in the morning while I was at work, my phone rang. It was the hospice representative I had talked to most often.

"I would like to ask you to stop by our office and sign a liability waiver," she said. "Your mother has fired us."

I had to admit I felt a bit proud of Mom. She had told me that she hated all the fussing and the touching and the hand holding and the fretting faces and the constant intrusion.

Early on in Mom's hospice care I told her, "You can tell whomever you want that you don't want this service. It's not mandatory. If you do not want hospice, then tell someone, but it should come from you."

So that's what the ol' gal did. She sent them packing and returned to her solitude and her dreams of another life.

I knew that a normal person would have loved the care and attention of the dedicated hospice providers. I could see that they tried so hard, but my mother was, well, that's just who she was, the most difficult person I had ever known.

Sixty-two

Within the past year there has been a dramatic change in my mother's personality, just as her neurologist had predicted. "Karen," she had said, "she won't always be like this, so angry and so violent. She's paranoid, and the antipsychotic drugs should help relax her some. Then, as her condition worsens and she heads into the later stages of Alzheimer's, she'll calm down. In the last stage she will lose control of her bodily functions, and there will be very little of her mind left. It's actually a good sign that she's so spirited, believe it or not. Means that she still has some of herself left."

"How long will that take, the later stages?" I had asked.

"No one can really predict that. Alzheimer's is a slow but progressive disease. It will eventually kill her if nothing else comes along first. It's rare that an Alzheimer's patient becomes as aggressive and violent as your mother is. It's even more difficult to predict when she'll move into the next stages of this disease."

"How many people are as combative as Mom?"

"No one knows that either. Many acts of violence among the elderly go unreported. Either they forget that someone hit them, or they're ashamed, or they're fearful that they might be separated from a lifelong partner who's become abusive, so they stay quiet."

But the violent Mom has disappeared. It began almost two years into her residence at the memory-care facility. Now when I arrive, she's happy to see me, and when I leave she thanks me for the coffee and tells me she looks forward to seeing me again. She's nice to the staff, and they tell me that they are amazed by the transformation.

She is in a deeper stage of her Alzheimer's now. She scored an eleven on her last MMSE test. One day she will not remember me, but I am assured that she will always have the best care. This summer she will be ninety-two. She catches the occasional cold but has been gaining weight. She's a bit chubby now, with a plump face and a poofy tummy.

I buy her new clothes and shoes from time to time, but she rarely wears any of these new things, especially the underwear. "I like my old stuff," she tells me. And that's fine. Mom will never get in trouble again. She can have her old undies, her mochas, and her chair in her quiet room.

We have grown confident that Mom will always be able to live at this facility. They genuinely love her and have many chuckles over stories about how difficult she's been. They call me when Mom is nice to them, just to let me know things are going well. Two of her caregivers have told me, "We do tend to love the feisty ones."

These people touch the residents' lives in a unique way. One of the senior staff members once said, "When they move here, we do fall in love with them. It's easy because we can only know them for who they are now. We don't know their histories. We don't know what they used to be like. We do not know the struggles you and others have had with them, so it's easier for us to love them fully and freely, without the cloud of pain or resentment."

Mom and I have had conversations about Dad, and it's clear she misses him. "He let me do almost anything I wanted," she says proudly. She has also told me that he apologized to her for his affairs. I am not sure if that really happened or not. I had long encouraged her to forgive Dad for her own sake, saying, "Carrying around baggage from the past serves no purpose. It only weighs down your future."

The reward for my sage advice? The dismissive wave.

"Mom," I remind her these days. "He chose you. I have no idea how many women Dad was involved with, and you don't really know that either. I do know that you are the one he stayed with and grew old with. You are the one he chose. That should mean something to you. You were the last person he talked to before he died. Do you remember what he said? He said, 'You're my wife.'"

Sixty-three

One day recently, as I was leaving Mom's room, she said, "Love you, Kiddo."

"Yeah, love you too, Mom."

"Bring coffee next time you come."

"Sure, Mom. See you in a couple of days."

I closed the door behind me and re-entered my life.

Epilogue

August 14, 1918–August 12, 2011

Lila Olivia McRoberts died on a sunny afternoon while taking a nap.

We visited her on August 11, and she was having such a good day. She was bantering with her caregivers and looking forward to her lunch. We brought her chocolate candy, which made her very happy.

On August 12, my husband and I were driving back from a day at the coast. Our car phone rang and it was the director of Mom's Alzheimer's care facility.

"I'm sorry to tell you … your mother has passed away."

On her last day Mom had her bath and her hair washed and then she had breakfast. Just after lunch she told her caregivers that she was going to take a nap. Around 12:30 they checked in on her and found her softly snoring.

They checked in on her again at 1:00 and she was gone, having quietly passed away in her sleep.

When I saw her for the last time I joked with her about her upcoming birthday and told her that we planned on seeing her on her big day. I also kidded her that she had now officially lived longer than Dad. He was fifteen days from his ninety-third birthday when he passed away and she was just three days away from her own ninety-third.

She stopped smiling, looked at me, and said, "Well now, isn't that interesting?"

Not knowing how to reply, I left it at that, feeling a bit uncomfortable that I had even made the comment. I hadn't expected it to be received so seriously.

Greg, Doug, and I will take my parents' ashes to the cemetery in Ketchum, Idaho, and place them there to rest. It was in Idaho that their relationship first began and they both expressed, at one time or another, that they'd like to return to the area.

Their headstone will be inscribed *It Happened in Sun Valley.*

This time, may they rest in peace.

Lila and Jim's headstone at the Ketchum Cemetery in Idaho. The design was created by the Wood River Chapel and Peck.

In Loving Memory

James Marvin McRoberts passed away on May 16, 2007.

He was born on May 31, 1914, in Sultan, Washington.
On January 5, 1942, he married Lila Olivia Hanka,
who grew up in Minnesota.

After living in Ketchum, Idaho he and Lila moved to Southern
California where he supported the war effort as a journeyman
machinist helping to construct fighter planes for Lockheed
Aircraft.

In the late 1950s he and his family moved to the San Francisco
Bay Area where Jim worked for Lockheed Missiles and Space,
contributing to the Gemini and the Apollo space programs.

Jim and Lila helped cofound Saratoga Country Club in the late
1950s where they enjoyed their many friends and played golf, a
game they both loved.

In 2005 Jim and Lila moved to Utah and then to Corvallis,
Oregon where they lived at West Hills Assisted Living
Community.

Jim is survived by his wife, Lila. They celebrated their 65th wedding anniversary on January 5, 2007.

Jim is also survived by his children, Greg Harvey McRoberts
of Milpitas, California, and Karen Olivia (McRoberts) Peck of
Blodgett, Oregon. Jim has two grandchildren, Stephanie Ann
Spencer of Portland, Oregon and Kristen Lynn Spencer of Palo
Alto, California.

Jim enjoyed a most fortunate life. He is loved and will be missed
by his family and his friends.

May he rest in peace.

Dearest Family and Friends:

August 14, 1918–August 12, 2011

On Friday, August 12, 2011, Lila Olivia (Hanka) McRoberts peacefully passed away in her sleep. We had just seen her the day before and looked forward to celebrating her upcoming 93rd birthday. We had lunch with her and she bantered with her caregivers, still feisty up to the very end.

On her last day she had a leisurely breakfast and spent time in the garden at her facility. Around noon she took a nap. When her caregivers checked in on her a half hour later she was sleeping peacefully. By one o'clock she was gone, passing away on a sunny afternoon.

After taking a summer break from college in the late 1930s, Mom and a friend took a train to the new resort of Sun Valley. Dad was working there and met Mom. After Mom returned to Minnesota, Dad went to work in Los Angeles. While Mom and Dad were apart they listened to national radio. One night the Glen Miller Orchestra played "It Happened in Sun Valley" and both Mom and Dad heard this song, he from L.A and she from Minneapolis.

Dad called Mom and proposed to her over the phone. She took a train to L.A. where they were married in 1942. Their marriage lasted for over sixty-five years. They played many rounds of golf at their favorite place, Saratoga Country Club and enjoyed traveling to many countries around the world.

My brother Greg, my husband Doug and I will take her and Dad's ashes to the cemetery in Ketchum, Idaho and lay them to rest. They first met in Sun Valley, ID and lived for several years in Ketchum. Both Mom and Dad expressed their wishes to return to Idaho as their final resting place.

Mom spent the past four years in an Alzheimer's care facility where she was loved and cared for. Her physical health remained strong so fortunately, she suffered no debilitating illnesses. She lived long enough to enjoy the arrival of her two great grandchildren whom she held and loved.

She always talked about her family and friends with such fondness and affection. Thank you all for loving her and remembering her.

Love, peace and gratitude,
Karen, Greg, Doug, Stephanie, Kristen, Isaac and Teagan,
her loving family

Images

My parents' wedding portrait, 1942.

Mom's high school graduation portrait, 1936.

Mom (right) and another waitress in Sun Valley.

Dad and another bartender at Sun Valley, 1947

Dad at Sun Valley: a possible publicity still for the resort (cropping out the fact that the skis are not touching snow).

Dad and Harvey Mink, one of his friends from Ketchum. My brother Greg Harvey was named after this man, who perished during World War II when his aircraft carrier was torpedoed by a Japanese submarine.

Dad, Ernest Hemingway, and Harvey, in Ketchum before the war.
The three men are holding a dead golden eagle by its wings. Its
stretched wings easily span all three men. The photograph is signed by
Hemingway to Dad:"Best to Jim from Dr. Hemingstein his pal."

Mom holding a huge rainbow trout; the photo was taken on one of her many journeys from Minnesota to Idaho, taking a break from college. I love the way her city suit contrasts so much with the old guy, the fishing shack, and that huge fish.

Mom, Greg, and I in L.A. just before moving to Idaho. Mom wrote on the back of this photo: "Greg 16 months, Karen 3 months. We look like savages."

Greg and I, Christmas 1948. He's three, I'm two.

Mom on a Los Angeles tennis court.

Mom and Dad on a tennis court in Los Angeles, 1948.

The stickers that Mom put on their wedding photo (Bye Jim—Love) and Dad's urn (Missing You). She did that several times with various objects. I will never know if his death registered with her, but the sticker on his urn and her handwritten comment seem to mean that she was trying to say something about his passing.

Author's Note

Alzheimer's disease has no known cause. It strikes every sixty-nine seconds. It is epidemic in people over eighty and can affect people as young as thirty. It is predicted to affect two billion patients worldwide by 2050. It is also predicted to bankrupt the American healthcare system by then.

Many snake oil "cures" for Alzheimer's are sold on the web, in books, and in magazine articles, yet there are no cures or treatments. Doing crossword puzzles, playing math games, or learning a new language cannot stop the progression of this disease. It is 100 percent fatal.

My mother was in an Alzheimer's facility for four years. Caring for her cost over a quarter of a million dollars. She never got better. She only declined, as all Alzheimer's patients decline. And then she died.

Alzheimer's patients are exploited. They are beaten and robbed, their assets embezzled by relatives and caregivers. They can also become abusers. While most patients do not act out, personality changes occur almost daily, and Alzheimer's sufferers can become unpredictable, violent, and dangerous.

There are many drug trials and research programs working to at least discover the cause of Alzheimer's or slow its progress. But for now, it is the incurable and untreatable plague of our time.

Please go to the Alzheimer's webpage, alz.org, for more information, a list of symptoms, and helpful suggestions for caregivers.

Kill Me First: The Dangerous Side of Alzheimer's by Karen Olivia Peck is available from amazon.com, barnesandnoble.com and lightningsource.com.

For book talks, contact Karen Olivia Peck on Facebook or by email at kpeck@peak.org.

All of Peck's presentations are free of charge.

Karen Peck lives in western Oregon with her husband, Doug, and her two dogs, Hattie and Cady. She is currently working on her next book.

Karen and Doug on vacation hiking Hadrian's Wall in northern England.

CPSIA information can be obtained at www.ICGtesting.com
Printed in the USA
BVOW010029100413

317761BV00005B/11/P

9 781467 504287